MATHEMATICS FOR THE MAJORITY

MACHINES, MECHANISMS AND MATHEMATICS

65

WITHDRAWN

MATHEMATICS FOR THE MAJORITY

MACHINES, MECHANISMS AND MATHEMATICS

§

CHATTO & WINDUS

LONDON

FOR

The Schools Council

1970

Published by
Chatto & Windus (Educational) Ltd.
42 William IV Street
London W.C.2

*

Clarke, Irwin & Co. Ltd.
Toronto

ISBN 0 7010 0455 X

Printed in Great Britain by
Robert MacLehose & Co. Ltd.
The University Press
Glasgow

Contents

Mathematics for the Majority

The Schools Council Project in Secondary School Mathematics (now called *Mathematics for the Majority*) was set up to help teachers construct courses for pupils of average and below-average ability that relate mathematics to their experience and provide them with some insight into the processes that lie behind the use of mathematics as the language of science and as a source of interest in everyday things.

Members of the Project Team (1967–70):

P. J. Floyd (Director)
K. C. Bonnaud
T. M. Murray Rust
E. T. Norris
Mrs J. Stephens
Mrs M. J. Talbot (to 1969)
P. Kaner (Evaluator)

The authors of this book are:

A. B. Bolt and J. E. Hiscocks

Introduction

This book has been written in the belief that much of mathematics has been developed to solve practical problems and that one motivation for doing mathematics will be to see its applications. Historically the great mathematicians have often been engineers who in tackling specific problems had to develop their own techniques which only later became abstracted and refined so as to be passed on to the next generation as ready made tools.

There is a great danger in much of the current reform in mathematics teaching that, as teachers, we learn about the refined tools in vacuo and pass them on to our pupils without ever knowing to what uses they can be put. The pupils we are interested in here will not be mathematicians or users of pure mathematics, but they will be living in a world which has been greatly influenced by mathematicians whether it is in the statistics of a Gallup Poll, in the design of a suspension bridge, or just in the design of a pedal bin.

Whether we look at the gears on a bicycle, the behaviour of a car jack, the motion of a rocking horse or the design of a washing machine we are dealing with objects which have been designed to fulfil a specific purpose. The shapes of the objects and the way their parts are related are highly significant and it is the belief of the authors that the study of these provides a realistic alternative to traditional geometry and that such a study can be both creative and rewarding.

It is hoped that this book will enable you to open your pupils' eyes to the abundance of engineering achievements in the world around and how to relate these to the underlying mathematical principles on which they were founded. In this way mathematics will be a part of life and not a set of symbols and techniques divorced from reality.

The main part of the book contains a wealth of material which could be used with pupils of varied ability, but it is in no way meant to be exhaustive. The first chapter suggests ways of using the material and should be read in conjunction with the other chapters.

Although the book appears at a first glance to be boy-centred the authors believe that there is also much here to interest girls.

Underlying the work which follows is the idea that we should do away with rigid subject boundaries for the mathematics here is as much concerned with history as engineering and is as full of practical work as aesthetic patterns. A project on the industrial revolution for example although normally thought of as history could equally well be seen as the triumph of technologists. The design of a new car is as much concerned with visual appearance as engine performance while safety factors and bodily comfort play an increasing role.

1

The Work and its Presentation

In the chapters which follow we have tried to give you, the teacher, a new approach to mathematics and because of this, it contains some examples at your level as well as some for the pupils. We have placed this chapter first because we see the success of the topics discussed later as being largely dependent on the classroom approach you use.

In studying the mathematics of machines and machinery, we are not aiming at some kind of fixed syllabus of work that must be covered nor do we suggest that particular topics should be studied until thoroughly understood. What is required is an over-all picture of the mathematics involved and the building up of an attitude to the subject, that allows the pupil to find matters of interest out for himself by means of observation and trial and error. In the early days of mathematics, particularly geometry, mankind studied problems by intuition backed up with experiments. It was not until the Greek schools of thought led by Thales, that rigorous proof was insisted on. We feel that much mathematics has been lost to the average child by its being shrouded in unnecessary formality. It is as if every car driver is being made to understand the full mechanics of the vehicle before being allowed to drive.

Thus bearing all the above in mind we want the pupil to find his facts out by sheer experiment and leave out all attempts at formal proof. It is the underlying principles we want him to understand, even if in some cases the understanding is at 'threshold' value.

Since few of the problems we put forward in the following chapters hinge explicitly on each other, there is no need for a strict order of work to be adhered to. We have given a guide to what mathematics can be achieved from the work at the end of each chapter — but do not let this limit you. If the teacher feels that certain experiments are sufficient for some particular principle to be grasped, then there is no reason why he should continue in the one direction merely because the authors have gone further or laboured a point more.

If the work is to be of any value then, each and every pupil must be allowed to experiment by himself and because of this, class teaching is not appropriate. The authors envisage small groups all working on different ideas with the teacher going around, advising or suggesting certain ideas but never telling. One way in which this work might be carried on is through the use of work cards. A more detailed analysis of these will be given later and examples are to be found at the end of each chapter.

This latter system has one other great advantage, namely that the amount of apparatus required will be no more than that required by the teacher were he taking the whole class together and demonstrating the results from a place in front of the pupils. This brings us now to the point of how the appropriate materials can be acquired. We do not intend the school to go out and buy all the necessary apparatus. Few schools could afford this kind of expenditure and, far more important, much can be learnt from assembling the various items for oneself.

To list a few items that will be required and how to go about it will, we feel, be a fairly general guide to all the materials needed. Bars for the linkages can be simply made from strips of cardboard, if additional strength is needed double thickness can be used. The fastenings can be paper clips and the holes punched out (see Fig. 1).

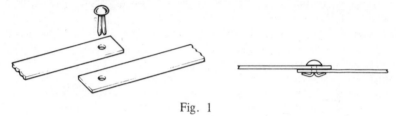

Fig. 1

If more stable versions are required then thin strips of wood can be used and small lengths of dowelling used for the joint (see Fig. 2).

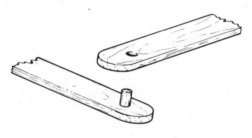

Fig. 2

These are not as satisfactory however as some commercial products such as Meccano, Bilofix or Geostrips (obtainable from Invicta Plastics Ltd, Leicester).

In time, a mass of suitable materials can be collected, much of which will be brought by the pupils. The latter are usually critical, especially if they can visualize the result expected, but the materials due to slight inaccuracies or poor quality do not give them.

2

Wheels, cogs and other similar items may be gathered together over a period of time. The large size plastic Meccano gears that are now made are ideal as are the plastic Bilotoy gears. Many machines such as dentists' drills use plastic or nylon cogs and these too are usually big enough for use. Work on the cycloids may be studied by using apparatus such as the 'Spirograph'. Failing this reasonable results may be obtained using cardboard wheels. Annular wheels being holes cut from thick card (see Fig. 3).

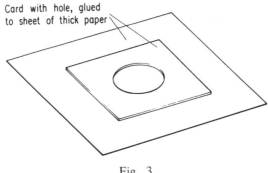

Card with hole, glued
to sheet of thick paper

Fig. 3

It will be found that the slightly jagged cut always made by scissors helps keep slipping to a minimum. If the inner wheel is only moved stage by stage this will not be noticed in the trace of the locus. It is however essential to glue down the non moving disc.

Three dimensional graphs can be either plotted using straws and pieces of plasticine or for more permanent models peg board and the appropriate sized dowelling. For the latter it will be found best to have two boards arranged as in Fig. 4.

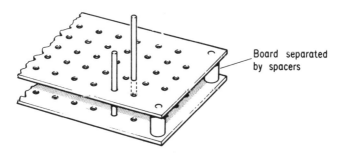

Board separated
by spacers

Fig. 4

The shapes for rolling experiments can be made out of normal hardboard or polystyrene.

3

There seems no good reason why, in the making of apparatus, the pupils themselves should not fully partake. The school workshop is just about as valuable an asset as an open cheque. Apparatus made by the pupils will be of far greater value to them than that made either professionally and thus bought, or that made by the teacher. As indicated before, in time a mass of material will soon accumulate and whilst this situation is most desirable it unfortunately brings with it a certain amount of chaos if not handled correctly from the start. Nothing is worse than pupils wandering about wasting time trying to find car jacks or cogs for their experiments from beneath heaps of assorted materials.

To each work card should be assigned a box with as much of the required apparatus as possible stored within it. Trays of equipment are best but boxes are sufficient especially the old chalk box type.

Certain items are either so large that they cannot be conveniently placed in a box or others so small or trivial that they soon get used up or lost. The former should be housed in a large and easily accessible cupboard or, as in the case of jacks, which might have to be borrowed, obtained well before the lesson. (Please note, the pupils themselves should be responsible for this and not their teacher). Small items, though seemingly trivial, are often essential in the work, and so such things as pins, elastic bands, coloured pencils and the like, should be stored in quantity in separate boxes and drawn on as required.

Nothing is more frustrating to a pupil than collecting the appropriate box only to find apparatus it should contain is missing. To avoid this, each box should be marked on the lid with its work card number and also with a list of items it should contain. Frequent checks should be made to see that the boxes do in fact hold what they are meant to. One school the authors have visited operated such a system and had the checking done by a group of fourth year pupils who took it in turns daily to issue equipment from the cupboard and check the boxes for faults in their contents. This idea has the added merit that the whole business is pupil operated and organised. This spirit is what is required and we would again emphasize the point that in all this work the pupil should be encouraged to play not only a full part in the actual lessons but also in helping the latter to run smoothly.

The teacher's job is the vital one of being a director, adviser and encourager.

We now turn our attention to work cards. Certain ideas are small in themselves, and so work cards set on them need not be lengthy. Other ideas however, are more complex and then we need to break the information down in a series of cards. For example, in the section on loci we take the packing case rolling along a flat floor (see chap. 6). Here it is required to study the loci of edge points, centre and internal points. Each of these ideas needs individual attention. Furthermore it will be seen that the actual practical work itself must be broken up, and not one but several cards used for the same topic. (The cards might be numbered, say, 12a, 12b, 12c and so on).

We believe that work cards, their wording and layout is very much an individual affair and we do not feel much is to be gained by printing a full series of such cards for all to use. As already noted at the end of each chapter, however, there are a few illustrations of work cards which we hope will be guides rather than finished and used products.

(For further ideas see the book *Assignment Systems* in this series.)

We suggest that in a sequence of work cards the first card should be highly structured — while subsequent cards become less and less so and should eventually lead to the pupil having to use his own methods for obtaining a result. In any situation that requires several cards instructions should be gradually reduced and the pupil asked to show his own initiative and imagination. Either way statements on the card should be definite.

To pupils new to the work card situation there will be an abundance of questions that they feel need to be answered, but in time it should be found that groups are able to work alone without continual guidance. The teacher should be able to spend considerable time getting groups to discuss their work, and, here too, much emphasis must be laid on the need for discussion not only between child and teacher but between child and child.

The teacher should not be depressed or put off by some (not necessarily all) of the work cards appearing to be too difficult for the pupils. A work card situation (i) takes some getting used to and (ii) wording of the cards is only perfected with time. Indeed, some pupils' inability to read may necessitate verbal instruction (some teachers have taped instructions). Continual modification to their layout and style should be made. It must be remembered that this kind of working requires much individual thinking on the part of the pupil and it is this as much as anything else, which we feel has been sadly missing from much of the mathematics work previously attempted at the secondary level.

Work cards which prove their value need preserving. If written even on thick card, they soon become dog eared, ink stained or worse still torn. In order then to prolong the life of a card it should be either pasted to a thin piece of hardboard and its surface covered with polythene or failing this the whole merely jacketed in polythene. This last method can be done quickly by merely having two sheets of polythene and stapling the card between them.

In the classroom these cards should be stored in racks with their numbers clearly visible and such that the pupils do not have to waste time searching for the appropriate card. Frequent checks should be made to see that they are returned in the correct order.

By this stage it should be apparent that good organisation plays an important role. Initially there is nothing but hard work for the teacher. It is the opening phase that might well deter many, but we would emphasize that once such a way of working has got under way it has many rewards. Of course it would be foolish to suggest that all will be milk and honey, there will be the inevitable crises but these are far outweighed by the triumphs and exciting discoveries that many children will make. Of the teachers who have already embarked on such a course, there are few who would return to only class teaching.

We now raise the question, do I start this work with the whole school? Such work as this is ideally introduced to the first and second years only and with the passing of time and the moving of these pupils up the school it will eventually be going on at all levels. However, this is relative, and we suggest that you start with one class and as you gain in confidence and experience (and acquire more apparatus) you infiltrate into other classes where appropriate.

It is not necessarily intended that every period of the week should be devoted to the work suggested. If you are new to a work card situation then experiment with a double period a week with one class for half a term.

Your way of working will depend on the space available.

Implicit in this way of working is the need for mathematics rooms — that is rooms in which mathematics is taught most of the time so that equipment is readily available and the walls can be used for display purposes. However do not use the lack of such facilities as an excuse for avoiding the issue.

Finally we suggest how the pupils may record their results.

The best idea is for each pupil to have his own folder in which he keeps either his exercise book or paper on which he has written the results of his findings. The authors prefer separate sheets of paper for each experiment which can be clipped together. These folders could be left in the classroom between sessions so that there is not the problem of coming to the next lesson without them.

In the actual write up of experiments, the pupils should be encouraged to answer all questions with short sentences of descriptive material and diagrams as well as give numerical answers. It seems unnecessary to have to describe the experiment carried out. It would be a nice idea to have duplicated copies of each work card so that the pupils could retain one each but this might not be very practical. A sketch of the apparatus, or of the set-up can often provide a sufficient description of the experiment.

Beyond this, the work is all a matter of personal approach and any method which helps the pupil to think for himself and become more aware of spatial relationships is of value.

Not all the experiments done need be recorded but there is a danger that pupils will see these lessons as pleasant time fillers without gaining much from them if nothing is recorded. Pupils who have difficulty in writing can be encouraged to give an oral exposition of their findings — perhaps a tape recorder could be used!

2

Linkages

This chapter explores the use of jointed rods in the world around us and begins to analyse their underlying properties by making simplified models of the situations. The first part of the chapter is intended to give an awareness of the wide usage of linkages, while the second part indicates how this wealth of material can be used in furthering pupils' spatial concepts.

By linkages we mean sets of jointed bars which are free to turn about their joints in two dimensions. These can readily be constructed by using commercially made apparatus such as Meccano, Bilofix and Geo Strip or just strips of card and paper fasteners. It is recommended that while reading this chapter you have some such equipment available, for it is only by handling a linkage and observing its parts moving relatively to one another that the action can be fully appreciated.

The Parallelogram Linkage

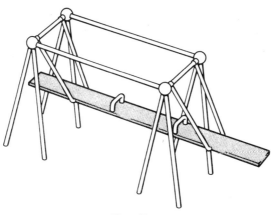

Fig. 5

The common children's playground toy in Fig. 5 illustrates clearly the parallelogram linkage which is used for many purposes. Although it is a three dimensional object all the motion is two dimensional so we can study it by making a simplified model of the essential parts as in Fig 6.

This technique of abstracting the essential parts and making a working model we shall use again and again to compare and contrast apparently different mechanisms.

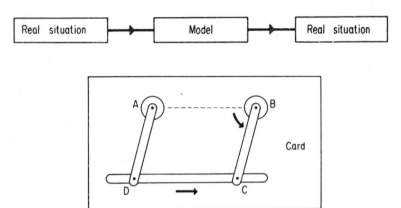

With A and B fixed, C and D clearly move in circles as AD and BC are of constant length.

How can we describe the motion of DC?

Does the motion appear different to a child sitting at an end to a child near the middle?

By making small holes in the strip DC on the model we can trace the locus for a variety of positions and we shall see that in each case it will be a circle with a centre on AB. Even though individual points of DC move on circles, DC always remains parallel to AB. (How does the braking mechanism of the swing work?)

Where else do we meet this linkage?

The two windscreen wipers on a car or lorry are often linked by a rod between their arms so that they are synchronised, otherwise they might collide. An example, not often seen now, is in the connecting rods between the driving wheels of a steam locomotive.

Anywhere where parallel motion is required this linkage is to be found and is exemplified by the instrument for drawing parallel lines (see Fig. 7).

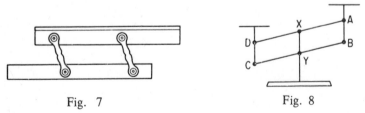

Fig. 7   Fig. 8

In the letter balance (see Fig. 8) the midpoints X and Y of AD and BC are fixed so that AB and DC are always vertical thus keeping the pans horizontal. Why? Compare this with a chemical balance; a see-saw; a pair of kitchen scales.

The sewing box with the extending drawers is a very good example of its use where the drawers themselves form the horizontal bars of the

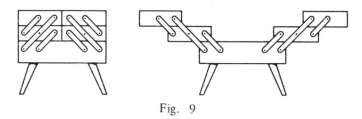

Fig. 9

linkage (see Fig. 9). The positioning of the brackets to obtain the correct amount of sideways displacement needs careful thought. A useful exercise would be to make a two dimensional model of such a box where the drawers are rectangles of card.

Why are the drawers relatively stable in the fully closed and fully open position? This is best answered by looking at the unstable intermediate positions.

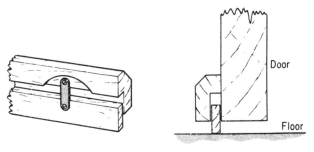

Fig. 10

Another domestic use is the spring draught excluder for the bottom of a door (see Fig. 10). Imagine a large version of the parallel rulers in Fig. 7 fixed to the bottom of the door with a spring to keep the movable part pressed on the floor.

The mechanism for moving the guide sprockets of a continental make of cycle gear also employs a parallelogram linkage, while it has also been used for the independent suspension of a car front wheels (see Fig 11).

9

In the latter one drawback is that the distance between the wheels changes, (Why?) and thus causes tyre wear.

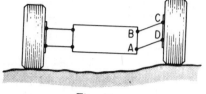

Fig. 11

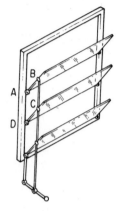

When several windows are to be opened together they are often linked as shown in Fig. 12.

Fig. 12

Venetian blinds work on a similar principle although then one set of parallel rods is replaced by strings.

This is by no means an exhaustive list but an attempt to show the varied ways in which the parallelogram is used.

The Quadrilateral Linkage

As soon as we allow the lengths of the bars to be different the variety and applications of a four bar linkage are enormous.

Compare the two rocking horses in Fig. 13. Their motion is produced in an identical way although the linkage in the larger one is completely

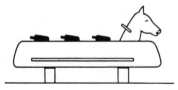

Fig. 13

hidden under the body. Fig. 14 shows the underlying linkage in a symmetric position and an unsymmetric position. Although DC is parallel to AB in the symmetric position, as it moves the angle between DC and AB is constantly changing.

What difference to the rider would it make if the rocking horse were based on the earlier linkage of Fig. 6?

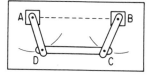 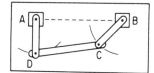

Fig. 14

The locus of D is clearly a circle about A, but do other parts of DC move on circles? This is a difficult question to answer analytically but by constructing a simple model the loci of different points of DC can be readily traced. A card cut-out of a rocking horse on curved runners can be made and the two motions compared. It should be a simple matter, for the practically minded, to construct a rocking chair using this linkage.

The same linkage is used for see-saws by the manufacturers of children's playground equipment. In this case the see-saw plank, which is long compared to the bars of the linkage, is fixed to DC, A and B being in the central pillar. This has the advantage that the plank stops turning when DCB is a straight line thus preventing the end from banging the ground.

Design a suitable linkage which will let DC turn through a maximum angle of 30° to AB.

If the only use of this linkage were in the design of good toys its mention would be justified, but the intriguing fact is that it is also essential to the steering mechanism of a car. When a car turns, the rear wheels are parallel (see Fig. 15) so to avoid side slip, the front wheels must turn to be at right angles to the line joining them to the centre of the turning circle. Why? This means that the direction of the front wheels must turn at a different rate, for when the car is on a straight course they are parallel. The way the linkage is used to achieve this is shown in Fig. 16.

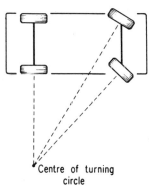

Centre of turning circle

Fig. 15

11

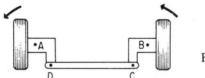

Fig. 16

The model is drawn in the symmetric position (compare with Fig. 14 and as the steering wheel is turned to the left the track rod is moved to the right causing AD to turn faster than BC. It can be readily observed on a toy pedal car or gokart while the linkage to produce the effect on the front wheels of a tractor can also be easily seen.

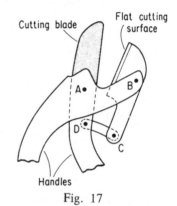

Fig. 17

Pruning shears make an ingenious use of the quadrilateral linkage (see Fig. 17). As the handles are squeezed together the cutting blade meets the cutting surface with a sliding as well as a pincer motion.

A similar linkage is used for attaching the bonnet of the Ford Cortina car (see Fig. 18) and on a larger scale for the hanging of an up-and-over garage door. Instead of a standard hinge the bonnet is attached to the body-work of the car by two rods AB and DC. As the bonnet is lowered CD turns anti-clockwise and the bonnet slides and turns into place with the same motion as that with which the cutting blade of the shears meets the cutting surface.

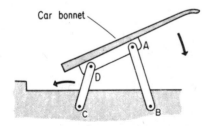

Fig. 18

In these days when space is at a premium, folding furniture has really come into its own. Whether we look at picnic chairs, folding beds or push chairs the required effect is inevitably produced by a linkage.

The sequence of diagrams in Fig. 19 shows just one way in which a push chair has been constructed so that it may fold flat — there are many others.

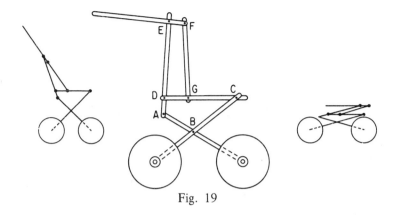

Fig. 19

The two quadrilateral linkages ABCD and DEFG are constructed so that they close up together. It is instructive to make a model of this one and any other you can examine to see their differences and similarities.

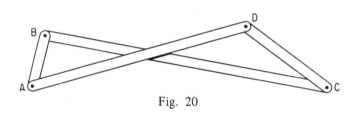

Fig. 20

An interesting adaptation of a quadrilateral linkage occurs when a pair of opposite bars are allowed to cross over one another (see Fig. 20). Two apparently unrelated objects, a pedal bin and a treadle sewing machine (see Fig. 21) turn out to depend on just this linkage.

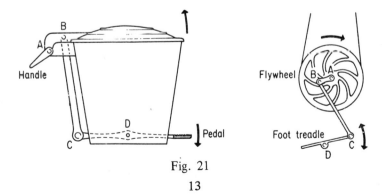

Fig. 21

13

A and D are the fixed pivots in both cases.

As the pedal of the bin is pressed, rod CD turns clockwise about D so that the rod CB pushes the lid anticlockwise about A.

With the treadle sewing machine B makes complete circles about A while DC 'rocks' about D so that sometimes ABCD is a crossover quadrilateral and sometimes not.

Try making a linkage to represent the treadle mechanism. Care is needed to get the correct proportions for the lengths so that without a very large change of angle of DC, AB makes a complete revolution about A. Take care too with the overlap of the rods.

With a hand sewing machine the human arm takes the place of the bars DC and CB. DC is the upper arm, C the elbow joint and CB the forearm.

Observe the motion of your arm when turning a handle.

The leg plays a similar role when cycling (see Fig. 22).

Fig. 22

Many doors in offices have mechanisms for automatically closing them. The drawings in Fig. 23 show one example of such a mechanism and we see that with the door and the door frame it is a quadrilateral linkage.

14

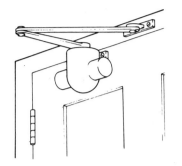 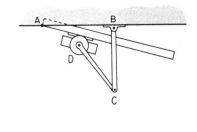

Fig. 23

It is clear that D traces out a circle about A as the door opens but does C turn clockwise or anticlockwise about B? What is the largest angle through which the door can be opened?

Much of the original interest in linkages came about when engineers tried to devise valve mechanisms for steam engines at the end of the 18th century. One problem which taxed their minds was to find a linkage which would produce straight line motion because at that time the technology was insufficient to produce metal slides with the necessary precision.

James Watt produced the first solution with a quadrilateral linkage (see Fig. 24) in 1784. By making AB equal in length to CD and both much longer than BC he found that the middle point M of BC traced out a path approximating to a straight line.

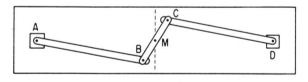

Fig. 24

Make a model of this linkage and see its limitations.

Tchebycheff in 1850 produced another quadrilateral linkage for the same purpose. In his version (see Fig 25) AB and DC are 5 units long, AD 4 units long and BC 2 units long.

15

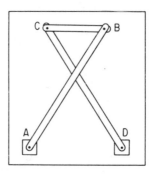

Fig. 25

Make a model of this linkage too and compare its limitations with Watt's design.

One of the most successful attempts at producing straight line motion was by a French army officer named Peaucellier in 1864. The linkage which takes his name (see Fig 26) has ABCD as a rhombus and OA = OC. When D traces out any circle which passes through O the locus of B will be a straight line. To confine D to a circle in a model just introduce a bar from Q to D. The theory behind this linkage concerns the transformation of 'inversion' with respect to a circle centred at O and is beyond the scope of this book.

However a model of the linkage is easily made and investigations can be carried out to see the paths traced by B when D moves on given paths.

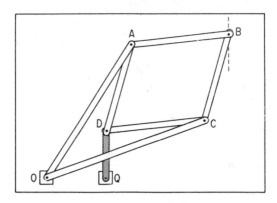

Fig. 26

Rhombic Linkages

So far the discussion had been about 4-bar linkages and we can extend still further by considering the kind of linkage often used for a lift gate which is a repetition of a linkage in the shape of a rhombus (see Fig. 27).

16

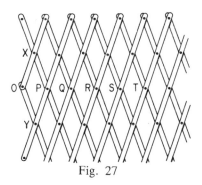

Fig. 27

With a model of this rhombic linkage the usual angle properties associated with parallel lines and the intercept theorems appear very clearly. By watching the linkage opening and closing it becomes apparent which are the constant factors (the invariant properties) and which are variable.

For example:

O, P, Q, R, S and T are always collinear.

OP = PQ = QR = RS = ST for all positions;

OP always bisects the angle XOY;

XY always bisects the angle OYP;

XY is always perpendicular to OP.

This network linkage is seen frequently as the trelliswork fence or on the walls of a house for training plants on but then its ability to change shape is not significant. However the folding clothes airer, lazy tongs and extending bracket are obvious applications of its properties (see Fig. 28).

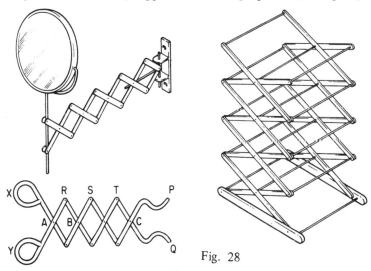

Fig. 28

17

When the handles X and Y of the lazy tongs are closed together what happens to the tips P and Q?

Skill is needed in the use of such tongs because of the considerable movement of PQ away from XY compared to the movement of X towards Y or P towards Q.

When the distance AB increases by 1 inch by how much does AC increase?

If X, Y are closed at a constant rate does AC increase in length at a constant rate?

Imagine A fixed and XY squeezed together symmetrically. What paths will be traced out by R, by S and by T?

Similar applications to those already mentioned are to be found in loft ladders, shop awnings and folding beds but a different application is found in the drawing instrument known as the pantograph for enlarging or reducing maps and drawings (see Fig. 29).

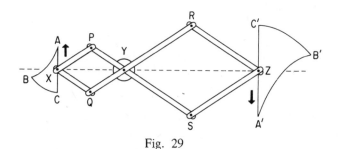

Fig. 29

In the example shown the linkage consists of two rhombi XPYQ and YRZS the second of which has twice the linear dimensions of the first so that YZ is always twice as large as YX and X, Y and Z are always collinear. When X traces out a shape such as ABC then Z traces out a similar shape A'B'C' which is twice as large but 'upside down'. A'B'C' is said to be an enlargement of ABC from centre Y with scale factor -2 — the negative because the direction of Z from the fixed point Y is opposite to the direction of X from Y.

Notice that if corresponding points of ABC and A'B'C' are joined the lines will always pass through Y and be trisected by it.

What is the area of A'B'C' compared with ABC?

How could you construct a linkage for producing an enlargement with scale factor of -3?

What is the locus of R as X traces out ABC?

By seeing the pantograph illustrated in Fig. 29 as part of the rhombic linkage in Fig. 27 we are able to see alternative linkages which would produce the same effect (see Fig. 30).

18

Of these (a) is probably the easiest to appreciate while (c) is the one which is often used in practice — it also uses the least material.

Make up these and other alternatives to satisfy yourself that they are all equivalent.

Could any bar of these linkages be removed so that the linkages still fulfil the same purpose?

All these linkages could be used to reduce a figure instead of enlarging it just by reversing the roles of X and Z. They are then said to give enlargement with a scale factor of $-\frac{1}{2}$.

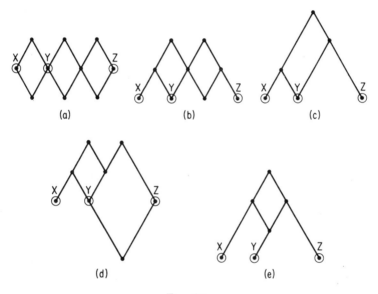

Fig. 30

How can we obtain a positive enlargement, that is an enlargement in which the image is the same way up as the object?

The answer is that we use the same linkage but fix X instead of Y. Fig 31 shows a practical application of a linkage used in this way.

When a small piece of metal or plastic for example has to be cut accurately, a large template is made of the correct shape and as Z traces around the template a tool or burner at Y cuts out the same shape on a reduced scale. In this diagram the scale is $+\frac{1}{3}$ because XY is always $\frac{1}{3}$ of XZ.

What would the scale be if Z was fixed and X used to trace the object and Y the image?

How can this linkage be used to produce an enlargement with a scale factor of $+3$?

19

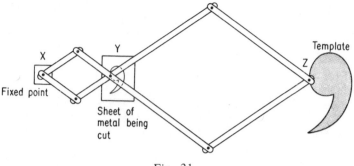

X

Fixed point

Y

Template

Z

Sheet of
metal being
cut

Fig. 31

If we pursue the study of the enlargement transformation we shall find
that when one enlargement is followed by another their combination is
equivalent to a single enlargement whose scale factor is equivalent to the
product of the individual scale factors. This incidentally gives us a very
good illustration of the products of directed numbers. If we take an
enlargement, for example, with scale factor -2 and combine this with an
enlargement with scale factor of -3 the result is an enlargement with scale
factor of $+6$. These results can be confirmed practically by combining the
linkages for the individual transformations. One way of doing this is shown
in Fig. 32. Notice that the three fixed points $0_1, 0_2, 0_3$ are collinear. Will
this always be the case?

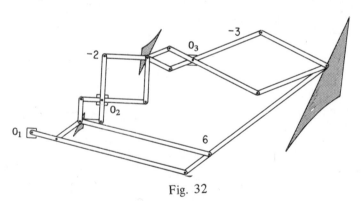

-3

0_3

-2

0_2

0_1

6

Fig. 32

The Variable Base Triangle

The linkage we shall consider now is perhaps the commonest of all
although it is different from the ones so far considered in that one bar of

20

the linkage is replaced by a component which can vary in length such as a spring, a screw, a hydraulic ram, or a slide (see Fig. 33).

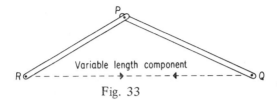

Fig. 33

When two rigid bars are linked in this way linear motion can be readily converted to rotation and vice versa.

The first example we look at is that of two car jacks. These (see Fig. 34) both work on the principle of shortening the base of an isosceles triangle by a screw.

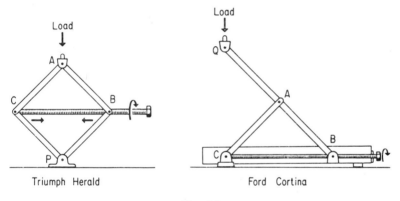

Fig. 34

Although the jacks appear different in form, their behaviour is identical for these linkages are both parts of the same rhombic net. The 'double rise' achieved with the Herald jack by having two isosceles triangles is achieved with the Cortina jack by extending arm BA to Q so that AQ = AB.

An interesting exercise is to plot the height of the jacks against the number of turns given to the screw. To start with, the jack rises quickly; but the rate of change in height slows down as the jacks get higher. This is a useful feature of this linkage for it means that when the jack is first put under the car and there is no load the jack is 'high geared' — but more of this later.

21

Contrast these jacks with a simple screw jack (such as that of a Mini) which is linear, that is, equal numbers of turns always give equal changes of height (see Fig. 35).

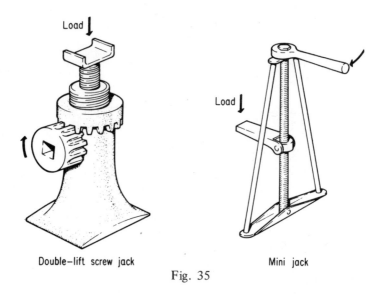

Double—lift screw jack   Mini jack

Fig. 35

Notice that the construction of the Mini jack is very simple and illustrates the importance of the triangle as the fundamental rigid structure.

It is instructive to make a model linkage representing the Cortina jack for it has many applications (see Fig. 36).

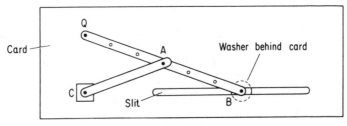

Fig. 36

If the model is held upright, as B moves horizontally towards C the point Q moves vertically from C. This is another way of saying that the angle QCB is always a right-angle. You can check this by noting that the

22

triangle AQC and triangle ABC are always isosceles and using the angle sum property of a triangle or alternatively by seeing A as the centre of a moving circle with diameter QB and using the angle in a semi circle result.

Why could not more lift be given to the jack by lengthening AQ? What is the snag? Examine the loci of points on BQ other than Q by putting a biro or pencil in the hole in the bar and tracing its path as B slides to and fro.

Compare the motion of the bar QAB with the motion of a ladder sliding down a wall (see Fig. 37). If A is always the mid-point of the ladder its locus is a circle, centre C. This matter will be discussed further in the section on loci.

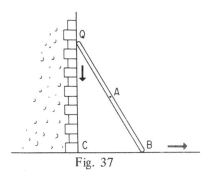

Fig. 37

The linkage in this form (AB = AC = AQ) is known as the Isosceles (or Scott-Russell) Straight Line Linkage because of its properties. It is in common use these days as the mobile jack in motor garages and as the stabiliser jacks on the corners of caravans.

When the two rigid legs are not necessarily equal the triangular linkage can be recognised in many other places as for example in the folding chair, deck chair, window fastening, window opening gear, motor-cycle suspension, independent car wheel suspension some of which are illustrated in Fig. 38.

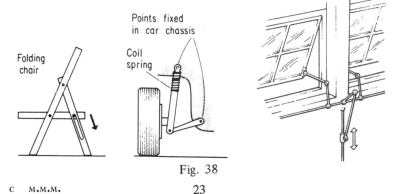

Folding chair

Points fixed in car chassis

Coil spring

Fig. 38

The fundamental linkage in many engine designs whether steam, petrol or diesel, is the crank and piston (see Fig. 39).

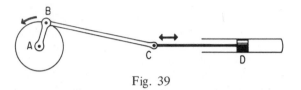

Fig. 39

As B makes complete circles about A the piston D reciprocates in the cylinder. In so doing the triangle ABC takes up all possible shapes consistent with AB and BC being of a given length.

When the length of AB is fixed is there any restriction on the length of BC?

On what does the length of the stroke of the piston D depend?

What locus is traced out by the mid-point of BC?

What is the maximum area of triangle ABC?

With an engine the initial energy comes from the explosion in the cylinder which drives the piston along and then the connecting rod CB converts this into the rotary motion of AB.

The first part of a mechanism is usually called the *driver* while the last part is called the *follower*. We can perhaps think here in terms of *input* and *output* for this has more general applications.

With the internal combustion engine the input is to the piston D and the output to the crank-shaft A. These roles are reversed with the car foot pump, the input is supplied to the rod AB and the output is to the piston (see Fig. 40).

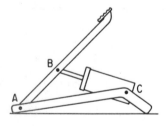 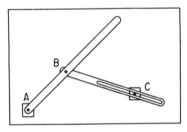

Fig. 40

Notice that because there is no connecting rod in the foot pump it is designed to allow the cylinder to oscillate.

The piston moving along the cylinder pushes air under pressure into a tyre.

One of the mechanisms being used more and more is the hydraulic ram which is rather like a pump in reverse. Oil under pressure is pumped into a cylinder thus forcing a piston along it and this when used in conjunction with a triangle linkage can be used to apply a couple (turning action) to a shaft. (In this chapter we are only concerned with the effect of a hydraulic ram and not how it works, this will be discussed later – see Chapter 4.)

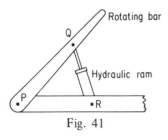

Fig. 41

This particular device is used time and time again in civil engineering machinery, agricultural machinery and transport whenever heavy loads have to be moved. By combining it with the right linkage a small hydraulic ram can be used to raise a jib, turn a bucket or tip a lorry.

In Fig. 42. a small selection of machinery which uses this device is shown.

In each of the examples a variable triangle PQR has been identified although there are others shown which are not labelled. Another feature of

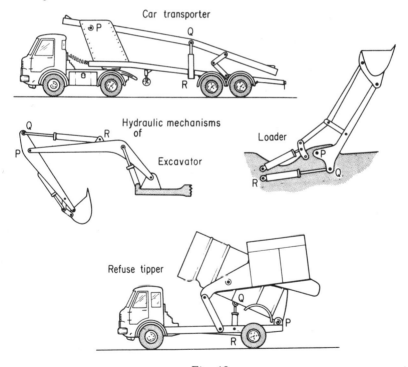

Fig. 42

25

all the examples shown is the use of a quadrilateral linkage and in one mechanism a pentagonal linkage occurs. Different makes of machinery feature different solutions to the same design problems but underlying them all is a linkage and a hydraulic ram. Further examples can be found by direct observation, writing to manufacturers for details of their plant or looking through magazines such as *Surveyor* or *Muck Shifter*.

The examples of mechanical arms on excavators is a reminder of the arms designed on a small scale for disabled people or for handling radio-active materials by remote control. All these ingenious inventions rely on linkages and hydraulic rams, but good as they are they cannot compete with our own arms. When looking at linkages it is suggested that comparisons are drawn with the human skeleton where appropriate. Be wary, however, of using the human skeleton as the starting point for it has too many degrees of freedom.

THE PUPILS' MATHEMATICS

Traditionally polygons have been studied as static figures and we have looked at their properties in this light. However if we view them as linkages we shall find that in addition to the usual properties others, such as rigidity, become significant.

Handling the bars of a linkage can give far more meaning to any geometric property than any amount of logical proof.

The property of a triangle that 'the length of two sides of a triangle are together longer than the third side' takes on significance when a pupil joins three rods **AB**, **BC** and **CD** of varied length end to end and sees under what conditions the free ends A and D can be joined (see Fig. 43).

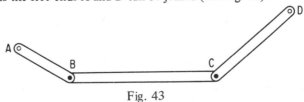

Fig. 43

This approach to a triangle also makes it clear why the standard ruler and compass construction of a triangle, given the lengths of its sides, works.

This chapter can be thought of as a starting point for any work on the properties of polygons you wish your pupils to discover.

When a 4-bar linkage has its opposite bars equal in length, the opposite bars are always parallel, the opposite angles are equal, and the diagonals (elastic is useful here) bisect one another.

When a 4-bar linkage has all 4 bars equal the diagonals are always at right angles and bisect the angles at the corner.

When a 4-bar linkage moves, one diagonal becomes longer, the other diagonal becomes shorter.

When one angle of a 4-bar linkage is made larger at least one of the other angles becomes smaller.

Linkages should lead to the concept of the triangle as the basic rigid figure and making polygonal linkages rigid by triangulation can lead to angle properties of polygons or simple surveying.

Tessellation linkages can lead easily into the properties of angles and transversals associated with parallel lines.

The pantograph can be used to do work on similar figures and linkages generally lead to work on loci.

Studying existing mechanisms can lead to an appreciation of spatial design problems and be far more meaningful than traditional geometry. This work is best done as a project in which a given mechanism is described and/or a model made of it.

The work must be practical and the following basic equipment is recommended before it is worth attempting this chapter with children.

 (i) Drawing boards, drawing pins and strips of stiff card in assorted lengths with small holes at 2 cm intervals.

or (ii) Geostrips and treasury clips — well worth buying.

or (iii) Meccano — metal or the larger plastic variety.

or (iv) Bilofix — wood, expensive and difficult to obtain, but good.

Drawing boards and card strips will probably be the cheapest way to start and these can be used effectively as shown in Fig. 44. A and B are fixed points with the drawing pins in the board while D and C are movable with the drawing pins point upwards.

It is helpful, as in the commercially produced materials, to have the card strips made in standard lengths with holes evenly spaced along them — this incidentally makes it easy to refer to the correct strips when using work cards.

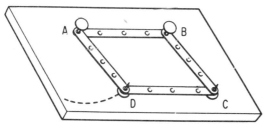

Fig. 44

27

The work cards which follow in no way exhaust the possibilities of this chapter but give some indication of how it might be used. Their wording will depend to a large extent on the kind of equipment available and the ability and age of the children. It is infinitely better to write your own!

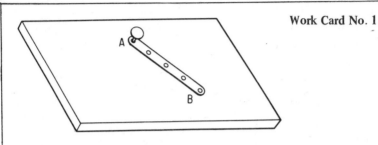

Work Card No. 1

Pin one end of a 5-hole strip to a drawing board. Place a pencil in the hole at B and move the strip about A. Repeat with the pencil in a different hole.
1. What name is given to the path traced out by the pencil?
2. How does the path change for different holes?

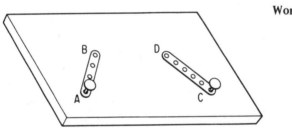

Work Card No. 2

Pin a 4-hole strip and a 6-hole strip to a drawing board so that they can turn about one end as shown.
1. Use a pencil to draw the paths of B and D as the strips turn.
2. Do the paths cross?
3. Can you join B to D with a drawing pin?
    Repeat by starting with A and C at different points.
4. What is the greatest distance that C can be from A if B and D can be joined?

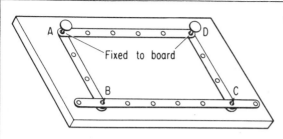

Make up a linkage with an 8-hole strip, a 6-hole strip and two 4-hole strips as shown and pin A and D to a drawing board.

1. Put a pencil in one of the holes in BC and trace its path as the linkage moves.
2. What is the shape of this path?
   Repeat for other holes in BC.
3. How do the paths for different holes differ?
   Give examples, with drawings, of the use of this linkage.

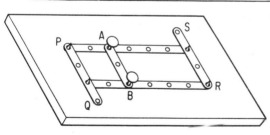

The linkage shown is made from two 4-hole strips, two 7-hole strips and a 3-hole strip. A and B are pinned to the drawing board.

1. As the linkage moves draw the paths of Q and S.
2. Which strips are always parallel to PQ?
3. When PQ moves down 3 cm what happens to RS?

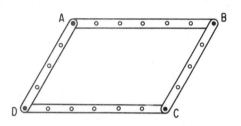

Use two 7-hole and two 5-hole strips to make a parallelogram linkage as shown.

Hold AB and move the linkage so that it changes shape.
1. What angle is always equal to angle ADC?
2. What happens to angle ADC as angle DAB gets bigger?
3. When angle ADC is a right-angle what do you notice about the other angles.
4. When AD turns clockwise about A what happens to BC?
5. Is DC always parallel to AB?

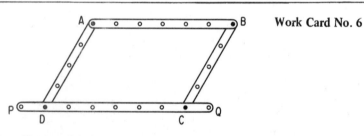

Use two 5-hole strips, a 7-hole strip and a 9-hole strip to make the linkage shown.

Hold AB and move the linkage so that it changes shape.
1. Name two angles which are always equal to angle BCQ.
2. Name two angles which are always equal to angle DAB.
3. What can you say about angle ADC + angle BCD?

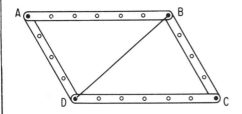

Make a parallelogram linkage as shown and join B to D with a piece of elastic (rubber bands could be used).

Hold AB and move the linkage to change its shape.

1. What is the greatest length the elastic is stretched to?

2. What do you notice about the angles ADB, ABD, BDC and DBC?

3. What happens to the length of DB as angle DAB gets bigger?

4. What happens to the length of DB as angle ADC gets bigger?

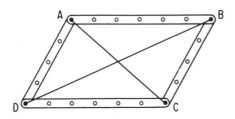

Make a parallelogram linkage as shown and join A to C and B to D with pieces of elastic.

1. Move the linkage so that AC becomes longer.

   What happens to the length of DB?

   What do you notice about the point where the pieces of elastic cross?

2. Draw the linkage when the pieces of elastic are the same length.

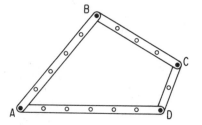

Make a quadrilateral linkage with 6, 5, 3 and 7-hole strips as shown.

Hold AD and turn CD clockwise about D.

1. Draw the linkage when
    (a) C is at its greatest distance from A,
    (b) C is at its closest point to A.
2. Draw the linkage when
    (a) angle BAD is largest,
    (b) angle BAD is smallest.
3. Describe the motion of AB as C makes complete revolutions about D.
4. If CD is replaced by a 5-hole strip could C turn completely around D?

Is it possible for all the angles of a quadrilateral to get larger at the same time?

Make a number of quadrilaterals and investigate.

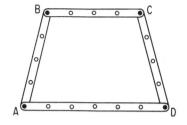

Make a linkage with three 5-hole strips and one 7-hole strip as shown.

Hold AD and turn AB clockwise.

1. Does DC turn through the same angle as AB?
2. Does BC remain parallel to AD?
3. Pin BC to a drawing board and investigate the path traced out by different points on AD.

Where is this linkage used?

Make a parallelogram linkage from 5-hole and 7-hole strips.

Find different ways of making the parallelogram rigid by joining another strip or strips to it.

Make a drawing of your answers.

Make different 4 and 5-sided polygonal linkages and find the smallest number of strips that have to be added to keep them rigid in each case.

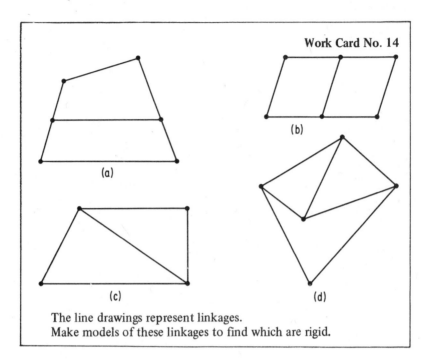

(a)

(b)

(c)

(d)

The line drawings represent linkages.
Make models of these linkages to find which are rigid.

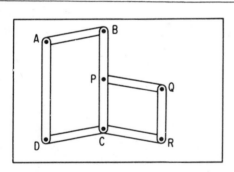

Make a linkage consisting of two connected parallelograms as shown and fix AD to the left hand side of a drawing board. Move the free part of the linkage around.

1. Is there any connection between angle ADC and any angle of parallelogram CPQR?

2. Draw lines along the edge of QR for different positions of the linkage.

What do you notice about these lines?

3. Where is this linkage used?

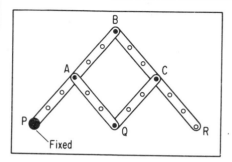

Make the linkage shown and pin the point P to a drawing board. This linkage is like a drawing instrument called the PANTOGRAPH.

1. Record the lengths of PQ and PR for different positions of the linkage. What do you notice?

2. Draw a simple shape in the middle of the board. Move the linkage so that Q traces out your shape and draw the path followed by R. What do you notice?

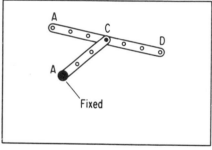

Make the linkage shown and pin it to a drawing board.

1. Move D along a straight line towards A and trace the path of B. What do you notice?

2. Move D along different lines and trace the path taken by B in each case. What do you notice?

Visit a childrens' playground and describe the apparatus you see there.

Make a model to show how one of the pieces of apparatus works.

Work Card No. 19

Examine a folding chair. Make a sketch of it and
either (a) make a model of it
or   (b) explain carefully how it works.

Work Card No. 20

Examine a pair of scales. Make a sketch of them and explain how they work.

Work Card No. 21

Investigate the steering mechanism of a toy pedal car and make a drawing or a model of what you find.

Work Card No. 22

Car Jacks

No of turns	Height of jack

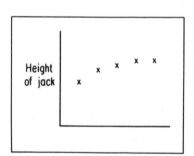

Borrow a car jack.

Turn the jack until it is as low as it will go.

Measure the height of the jack as you wind it up and record its height for different numbers of turns.

Plot a graph showing this information.

Repeat for different kinds of jack.

What differences do you find?

3

Transmitting Rotary Motion

In machinery we are often concerned with transmitting power from one revolving shaft (the driver) to another (the follower) and depending on the design specifications we might want to increase or decrease or vary the speed of the follower in comparison with the driver. The transmission of this motion can be achieved in many ways but they all have common features.

Pulleys and Belts

A look under the bonnet of most cars will reveal a fan and dynamo driven by a belt over a pulley on the engine shaft and around pulleys on the fan shaft and the dynamo.

Investigation of the underside or inside of a spin dryer or washing machine will usually reveal a belt driven from an electric motor to the moving parts of the appliance.

The question which most concerns us here is the direction and speed of the follower compared with the driver and we can investigate this experimentally by using a selection of meccano wheels and belts, for example, or making some simple pulleys from plywood discs. (In doing the latter it is best to make the discs relatively large, that is 2 inches diameter upwards.)

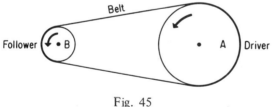

Fig. 45

With a simple arrangement like that in Fig. 45 we know that the speed of rotation of B and the speed of rotation of A are connected by the statement

$$\frac{\text{Speed of rotation of B}}{\text{Speed of rotation of A}} = \frac{\text{Diameter of A}}{\text{Diameter of B}}$$

but our pupils might not find this obvious and they will need to build this up through practical experience using pulleys whose diameters bear a simple ratio one to another. Arguments based on the distance moved by the belt along its own length will mean nothing to a child who has not accepted the result intuitively from experience.

The direction of motion can be reversed by giving the belt a twist as shown in Fig. 46. It might suggest asking what happens when further twists are given.

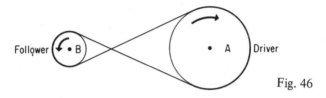

Fig. 46

To distinguish between the two cases illustrated where the change in speed is the same but the direction is different it is useful to have the concept of a *transmission factor* defined as follows:

The transmission factor from A to B is the number of revolutions made by B when A makes 1 revolution clockwise. The transmission factor is writen $\widetilde{AB}$, A indicating the driver.

An anticlockwise revolution is considered to be negative. (Note that in mathematics an anticlockwise angle is considered to be positive but the pupils we are interested in with experience of bearings and the motion of a clock expect the opposite and there seems no reason why we should not adopt the above convention.)

In Fig. 47 $\widetilde{AB} = 3$ while $\widetilde{CD} = -2$.
What are $\widetilde{BA}$ and $\widetilde{DC}$?

Fig. 47

In Fig. 48 pulleys B and C are fixed to the same shaft so that they turn together, thus $\widetilde{BC} = 1$.

What are $\widetilde{AB}$, $\widetilde{CD}$ and $\widetilde{AD}$?

With the same pulleys as in Fig. 48 connect AB and CD with direct belts and again find: $\widetilde{AB}$, $\widetilde{CD}$, $\widetilde{AD}$.

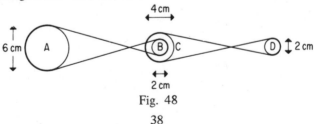

Fig. 48

38

Design a simpler pulley system which has the same overall effect.

You will soon appreciate that transmission factors have a notation like vectors and an algebra equivalent to the multiplication of directed numbers.

In Fig. 49 $\widetilde{AB} = -\frac{1}{2}$, $\widetilde{BC} = 1$ and $\widetilde{AC} = \widetilde{AB} * \widetilde{BC} = -\frac{1}{2}$ where * is used for the combination of AB and BC.

$\widetilde{CD} = 4$ and $\widetilde{AD} = \widetilde{AC} * \widetilde{CD} = -\frac{1}{2}x + 4 = -2$.

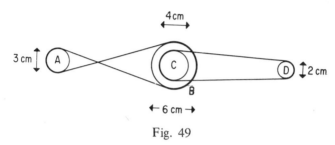

Fig. 49

You need not pursue the notation to any extent but the underlying structure is important and will be seen to tie in closely with gear trains.

One use of a belt which will be familiar to the boys will be in the workshop where there is a lathe requiring a variable speed. This is achieved by having two sets of pulleys as illustrated in Fig. 50 for example. When the belt is on A and P the lathe will be turning faster than the motor. When the belt is on B and Q the lathe and motor turn at the same speed and when the belt is on C and R the lathe is slower than the motor.

To make this a practical proposition the same belt needs to be used whichever gear is required.

This leads naturally into a consideration of the belt between two pulleys when the distance between their centres and their radii are known (see Fig. 51).

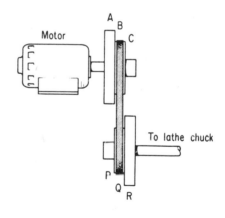

Fig. 50

The exact calculation of the belt length is reasonable when the pulleys are the same size but when they are different diameters the problem is of quite a different nature and resort will have to be made to scale drawings

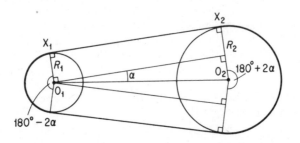

Fig. 51

and measurement. There are several properties of the resulting figure which are worth exploring en route, for the belt always takes up the common tangent position.

It will be found that within reasonable limits, for fixed centres O_1, O_2 the belt length remains approximately constant as long as $R_1 + R_2$ is constant. This means that in Fig. 50 for example the diameters of A, B, C, P, Q and R cound be 10, 8, 6, 6, 8 and 10 cm respectively.

What would be the values of $\overset{\frown}{AP}$, $\overset{\frown}{BQ}$, and $\overset{\frown}{CR}$ in this case?

To avoid this restriction on the pulley sizes the motor itself may be easily movable or a tensioning pulley may be used (see Fig. 52).

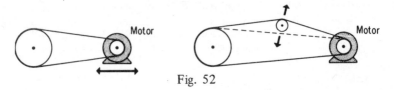

Fig. 52

The idea of block pulleys to give a variation in transmission factor is carried to the limit in the Daf car where instead of a gear box the drive is by a belt which carries the power from the engine to the rear wheels by means of a continuously varying gear ratio best illustrated by the cone pulleys in Fig. 53. The engine speed is kept more or less constant and the

gear is changed continuously by moving the belt from left to right. At the left hand end the car is low geared while at the right hand end it is high geared. This is an interesting example where an improvement in belt technology has enabled a manufacturer to return to a type of transmission used on the very first cars when it suffered from breaking belts. It is now being tried out in grand prix racing cars where it is found capable of transmitting up to 500 b.h.p.

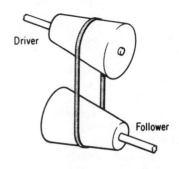

Fig. 53

40

Why is it best to use a belt with a twist in it (see Fig. 54)? (Consider the wear that takes place on such a belt.)

Fig. 54

Sprockets and Chains

Closely related to the belt and pulley transmission is the chain and sprocket which is so familiar on the bicycle and forms a halfway stage between pulleys and gear trains.

In Fig. 55 suppose the driver has 36 teeth and the follower B has 12 teeth, then AB = 3.

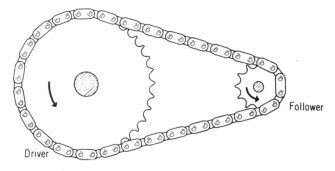

Follower

Driver

Fig. 55

Because the teeth and the links in the chain can be counted it is more appropriate to back up practical experience (bicycles and Meccano) by considering the number of links which pass a given point when A makes one revolution and from this deduce the number of revolutions made by B. Because a chain does not slip it is used in preference to a belt when synchronisation of linked shafts is important.

41

A typical gear ratio on a cycle is achieved with a 45 toothed crank wheel and an 18 toothed free wheel. This gives a transmission factor of $\frac{5}{2}$.

How far does a 26 inch bicycle wheel travel forward for one revolution of the crank wheel using this gear?

Racing cyclists favour variable gears where the freewheel is replaced by a block of between 3 and 5 different sized wheels, with a mechanism for moving the chain from one end to another, and wheels P and Q to ensure that the chain is kept taut (see Fig. 56).

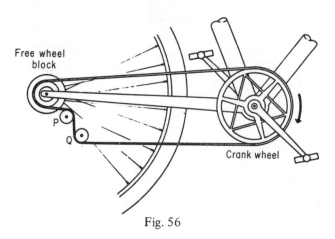

Fig. 56

What are the transmission factors when the crank wheel has 42 teeth and the block has sprockets with 14, 18 and 21 teeth respectively? Which would you use (a) going up a hill and (b) on level ground with a following wind?

Cyclists trying to break the world speed record (approximately 130 m.p.h.) have had to design very high gears. How would the crank wheel have to be changed to give a higher gear? How would the free wheel have to be changed to give a higher gear?

Both these wheels are limited by physical considerations. What are they? Can you estimate what the highest transmission factor obtainable with a standard cycle would be?

Gear Trains

Even before modern technology enabled us to manufacture gear wheels to a high degree of precision, the ideas existed with wooden dowels as illustrated in Fig. 57. These are still used in primitive civilisations today.

Experiments can readily be carried out with sets of gears particularly now that Meccano have produced a very good set of plastic gears which are large and easy to handle — their brass ones are good but because the teeth

42

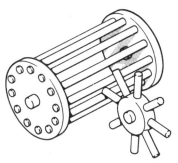

Fig. 57

are small they are not easy to count accurately. Again the transmission factor is relevant and its numerical value is seen to be equal to the ratio of the numbers of teeth on the wheels.

In Fig. 58 $\widehat{AB} = -2$, $\widehat{BC} = -\frac{3}{2}$ and $\widehat{AC} = \widehat{AB} * \widehat{BC} = -2 \times \frac{3}{2} = +3$.

One important result to establish here is that, when an odd number of gears are enmeshed the transmission factor is positive whilst with an even number it is negative.

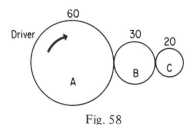

Fig. 58

The number of gears between the driver and the follower only effects the *sign* of the transmission factor.

What is perhaps surprising is that the magnitude of the transmission factor is independent of the intermediate gears.

This result is perhaps a surprise at first but a few calculations with simple examples makes it apparent.

A couple of worked examples should make the reason apparent.

In Fig. 59(a)

$$\widehat{DF} = \widehat{DA} * \widehat{AB} * \widehat{BF} = \frac{-32}{16} \times \frac{-16}{12} \times \frac{-12}{64} = \frac{-32}{64} = \frac{-1}{2}$$

while in Fig. 59(b)

$$\widehat{DF} = \widehat{DC} * \widehat{CF} = \frac{-32}{25} \times \frac{-25}{64} = \frac{32}{64} = \frac{1}{2}$$

43

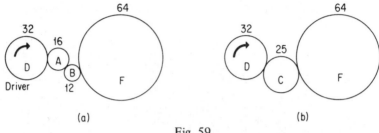

(a)   (b)

Fig. 59

In practice the actual gears used to give a desired transmission factor will depend on the relative positions of the drive shaft and the following shaft as well as the standard gears available.

A simple reversing mechanism used in some toys depends on introducing a second cog between the driver and follower (see Fig. 60).

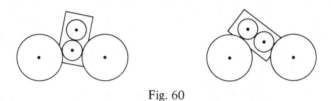

Fig. 60

The foregoing would make it appear impossible to get a very high or very low gear without using a very large gear with a very small one. However this can be overcome by using two wheels on the same shaft.

The gear train in Fig. 61 has a transmission factor of 20 because:
$$\overset{\frown}{AD} = \overset{\frown}{AB} * \overset{\frown}{BC} * \overset{\frown}{CD} = -4 \times 1 \times -5 = 20.$$

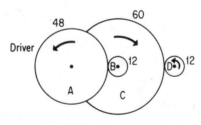

Fig. 61

To achieve this with just three gears would require one with a very large number of teeth because it is not practical to have the smallest wheel with fewer than about 12 teeth. What does this imply about the driver wheel? (Remember the middle one is only to reverse the direction of the turn and any practical size will do.)

The gear train in Fig. 62 illustrates how to achieve a low transmission factor and also shows that the shafts do not have to be in line. A close examination of a clock or watch is of interest to see how the transmission factor of +60 is achieved between the shaft for the hour hand and the shaft for the minute hand.

Is $\widetilde{AF}$ positive or negative?

Suggest numbers of teeth for A, B, C, D, E and F so that the numerical value of $\widetilde{AF}$ is $\frac{1}{72}$.

In a well designed gear train to achieve a given transmission factor it is best to have the intermediate transmission factors approximately equal (can you suggest why this is the case?), so for example if it is required to achieve a factor of +30 using

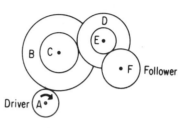

Fig. 62

four wheels, two of which are on the same shaft then the solution as shown in Fig. 63 (a) is better than that shown in Fig. 63 (b).

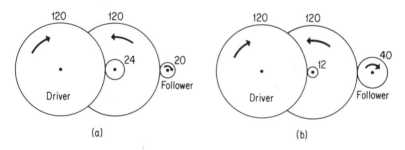

Fig. 63

Design a gear train with transmission factor of $+\frac{1}{150}$ given that the standard gear wheels available are: all tooth numbers from 12 to 24, all even numbers from 24 to 100 and every fourth number from 100 to 120.

Investigate the gear trains in a high speed bench grinding machine or an electric drill.

Gear trains of the kind so far considered are the best practical solution when the shafts being turned are parallel and relatively close together and are the basis of a car gear box (see Fig. 64).

Fig. 64 shows how the different transmission factors in a 3 speed gearbox are achieved. The shaft carrying gear wheels 3 and 5 is not fixed to the drive shaft which carries gear wheel 1 but is in line with it. It is a

45

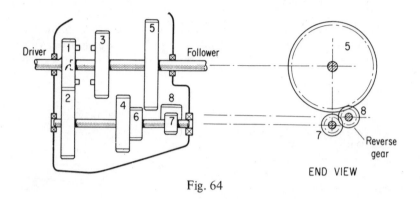

Fig. 64

shaft with grooves in it which allow the wheels 3 and 5 to slide along it but ensure that these wheels turn with it.

The gear wheels 2, 4, 6 and 7 are permanently fixed to the lower shaft and turn whenever the drive shaft is turning because 1 and 2 are permanently enmeshed. Thus power from the engine is first transmitted to the lower shaft and then back to the shaft carrying gear wheels 3 and 5.

1st gear is achieved by sliding gear wheel 5 to the left to enmesh with gear wheel 6.

2nd gear is achieved by sliding gear wheel 3 to the right to enmesh with gear wheel 4.

Top gear is achieved by sliding the gear wheel 3 to the left until lugs on its side engage with lugs on the side of gear wheel 1 thus giving a direct drive.

Reverse gear is achieved by sliding the reverse idler gear wheel 8 to the left so that it enmeshes with gear wheel 5 whilst still being enmeshed with gear wheel 7.

Investigate possible transmission factors for such a gear box by giving values to the numbers of teeth on the gear wheels. (N.B. as the number of teeth on a wheel will be proportional to the diameter it follows that the total number on 1 and 2, 3 and 4, 5 and 6 must be the same.)

Top gear being a direct drive cannot be altered but the others can all be adjusted independently or together by changing gear wheels 1 and 2.

Design a gear box in which the direct drive does not give the highest transmission factor.

Transmitting Rotation Between Perpendicular Shafts

So far with belts, chains and gears we have been concerned with parallel shafts but in many applications of gears, the shafts are perpendicular. To achieve this a large variety of gears have been designed some of which are illustrated in Fig. 65.

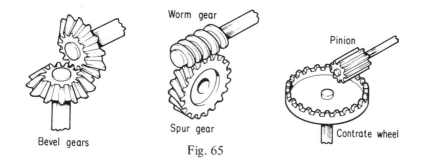

Worm gear

Pinion

Spur gear

Contrate wheel

Bevel gears

Fig. 65

Bevel gears are easy to appreciate and are found for example in a hand drill (see Fig. 66) or the drive to the automatic wringer of some washing machines. The worm gear is not so common but is usually used for producing a large reduction in gearing.

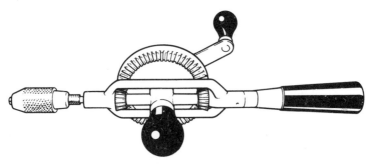

Fig. 66

The worm gear must be used as the driver and when it is enmeshed with a spur gear, for example, the gear ratio will be equal to the number of teeth on the spur gear, as the latter gear will only move on one tooth for every revolution of the worm gear.

The authors have successfully used a Meccano gear of this type to reduce the high revolutions per minute of a small diesel engine to a speed where it could drive the rear wheels of a model car.

The contrate wheel can frequently be seen as the driver in the mechanism for an egg whisk.

How is the drive transmitted from the wheels of a lawnmower to the cutting blades?

What kind of gears are used on a fishing reel?

If possible dismantle a hub gear from a cycle and examine it. How are gears used in a hand calculating machine? How does a cyclometer work?

Gears – What next?

There are many directions in which the study of gears can be taken, depending on the interest and ability of the reader, and availability of materials. Two possibilities are mentioned briefly below:

(a) *The shape of the gear teeth* to ensure normal contact of the enmeshing teeth and a constant transmission factor needs careful design and leads to a study of a variety of interesting curves.

(b) *Gears to provide variable transmission factors* are achieved by using non circular gear wheels such as the elliptic gear wheels in Fig. 67. A detailed study of these is fascinating but perhaps too demanding for the pupils we are concerned with.

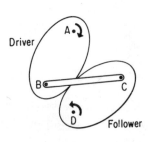

Fig. 67

A, B, C and D are the foci of the ellipses. As the driver turns around A it is kept in contact with the follower by the link rod BC. A model can be made of this using plywood ellipses whose edges have been roughened by sticking a strip of coarse sandpaper or rubber around them.

For an elementary approach to these topics a useful reference is *Mathematical Models* by Cundy and Rollett, (O.U.P.) A more detailed analysis of these and many other topics can be found in books such as *Analysis and Design of Mechanisms* by Deane Lent (Prentice Hall).

THE PUPILS' MATHEMATICS

There are some fundamental spatial concepts in this which most pupils can grasp:

(a) When a large wheel drives, or is driven by, a small wheel the large wheel turns through a smaller angle than the small wheel.

(b) Two pulley wheels linked by a belt turn in the same or opposite direction depending on whether the belt is uncrossed or crossed.

(c) When two gear wheels are meshed they turn in opposite directions.

(d) The amount of turn of one wheel compared to another can be calculated from their dimensions.

48

The term 'transmission factor' and the signed numbers need not be for use of the pupils. They were introduced to show how an algebra can be invented for a given situation. The pupils may well use the more familiar gear ratio along with 'clockwise' and 'anticlockwise' for the direction of turn.

In all mechanisms it is necessary to distinguish in which part the motion starts (the driver) and which part gives the output (the follower). When this is known the relative movement of the two parts can be calculated as a scale factor (in this instance a gear ratio) and this is usually a significant part of the design of the mechanism.

EQUIPMENT

This is not so easily made for this chapter, but wooden pulleys (the larger the better) can be cut out of plywood in the woodwork department and mounted on a board as shown (Fig. 68).

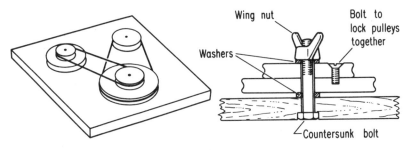

Fig. 68

Belts can be made from string or elastic. Wing nuts will make pulleys easily changeable, and with half a dozen pulleys and belts of assorted sizes a large variety of experiments are possible. In many ways this is better than buying Meccano pulleys and belts. Gear wheels however are probably better bought commercially. Meccano produce small precision brass cogs but the larger plastic ones are probably better and come as a kit complete with base-board. Bilotoy produce better plastic gears however if you can obtain them.

Friction usually prevents more than 3 gear wheels in a gear train turning, but this should be sufficient to grasp the concepts involved.

In addition to the spatial concepts mentioned there is clearly work here involving counting, measuring lengths, angles and handling fractions.

The small selection of work cards which follows gives some indication of the possibilities.

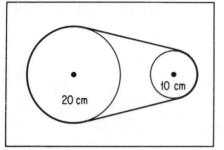

Fix 20cm and 10cm pulleys to a base-board as shown.
Turn the larger pulley around once, clockwise.
1. Which way does the smaller pulley turn?
2. How many times does the smaller pulley turn around?
3. When the smaller pulley turns around 6 times how many times does the larger pulley turn around?
4. Which pulley turns the faster?
Repeat using 15cm and 5cm pulleys.

As for Work Card No. 23 but with the belt crossed.

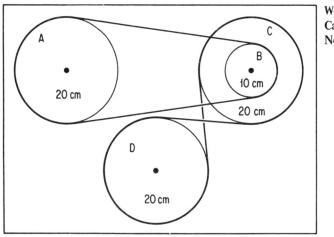

Arrange 4 pulleys on the base-board as shown.
1. When A turns clockwise in what direction does D turn?
2. When A turns around once, through what angle does D turn?
3. Show how the belts can be changed so that D turns the same way as A. Draw a diagram of your answer.

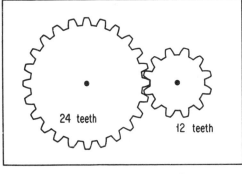

Arrange two gear wheels to mesh as shown.
1. Turn the larger wheel clockwise.
In which direction did the smaller wheel turn?
2. How many turns does the small wheel make for the large wheel to turn around 3 times?
3. Does the large wheel turn faster or slower than the small wheel?

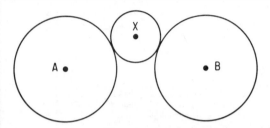

Take two equal gear wheels A, B and mount them so that they each mesh with a third wheel X as shown.

Turn A and see how the other wheels move.

1. Does B turn in the same direction as A?

2. How many times does B turn when A turns once?

Repeat with a different size wheel in the middle.

What do you notice?

---

1. Design a gear train with a gear ratio of 2 so that the follower turns in the opposite direction to the driver.

2. Modify your design so that the follower turns in the same direction as the driver.

Make careful drawings of your designs.

Examine a hand-drill or an egg-whisk.

Make a sketch of it.

Work out its gear ratio.

How could you modify the design to give it a higher gear ratio?

How are different speeds arranged on a lathe (or a potter's wheel) which is driven by a constant speed electric motor?

Investigate the use of pulleys and belts in farm machinery.

4

Rotary and Linear Motion Combined

Pulley Systems

One of the simplest ways of transmitting linear motion is to make use of a wire or rope over a system of pulleys. In Fig. 69 all the pulleys are free to turn about fixed axes. How far does Q move when P is pulled through 1 metre?

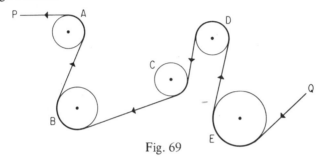

Fig. 69

No matter how many pulleys we have in a system like this, or what size they are, the distance moved by Q will always be equal to the distance moved by P.

Although there are occasions when we want to keep the distances moved by P and Q the same, there are many more instances where we want to scale, up or down, the movement of Q relative to P.

Consider the two pulley systems in Fig. 70. In each of these one end of a rope A is fixed and the rope passes around a movable pulley block Q and over a fixed pulley block B. How far would P have to be pulled to raise Q through a height of 1 metre? (Note the 'strings' on both sides of Q will be shortened).

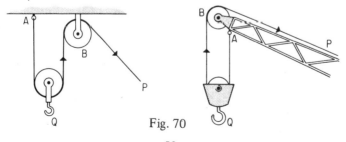

Fig. 70

53

How far does Q move in comparison with P? We could usefully take up our idea of a transmission factor again and define it as:

$$\text{The linear transmission factor of the system} = \frac{\text{Distance moved by Q.}}{\text{Distance moved by P.}}$$

In this case it is $\frac{1}{2}$.

Why is it not appropriate to use directed numbers in this case?

By increasing the number of pulleys on a block the transmission factor can be made smaller. The system illustrated in Fig. 71 consists of two pulley blocks each containing 2 pulleys. The upper block is fixed while the lower block can move.

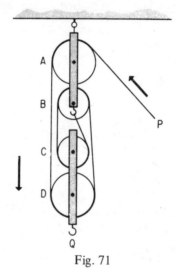

Fig. 71

When Q moves down 1 metre how many 'strings' have to be increased in length by 1 metre? How far does P move?

From your answers to these questions you should see that the linear transmission factor of Q relative to P is $\frac{1}{4}$.

A simple system is shown in Fig. 72 consisting of a shaft carrying winding drums of different sizes. (N.B. the shaft could be vertical and there is no need for P and Q to move in parallel directions). If the drums are of radii a and b then on the completion of 1 revolution P will have moved a distance $2\pi b$, equal to the circumference of the drum, while Q will have moved $2\pi a$, similarly, so that the linear transmission factor of P relative to Q will be

$$\frac{\text{Distance moved by P}}{\text{Distance moved by Q}} = \frac{2\pi b}{2\pi a} = \frac{b}{a} \, .$$

What is the transmission factor of Q relative to P?

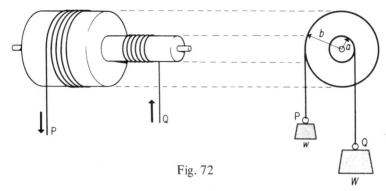

Fig. 72

A system like this could be made up using a cotton reel on a small wooden dowel for example although if a lathe is available a more professional system could be turned.

Often the point of a pulley system is to enable a small force to move a larger force and this can be the basis of some experiments. A weight W can be attached at Q and the smallest weight w which when attached to P will just raise W is recorded. This can be repeated for a variety of weights and the results tabulated and plotted. If the pulley system were ideal then

$$\frac{w}{W} \text{ would be constant and equal to } \frac{a}{b}$$

In practice (because of friction) the w needed to overcome a given W is larger than this, but as a guide to what to expect of a pulley system the transmission factor is important.

The nearer $\frac{w}{W}$ is to $\frac{a}{b}$ the more efficient is the pulley system.

The above pulley system and the Weston Differential Pulley System illustrated in Fig. 73 give plenty of scope for experimental work leading to graphs as well as work on the circumferences of circles.

The two pulleys at B (Fig. 73) are joined together and their radii differ by only a small amount so that as B turns the length of chain taken up by the larger wheel is only slightly more than that dropped by the smaller wheel.

If the radii of the wheels at B are r and R then after 1 revolution the loop of chain around A will have changed in length by $2\pi(R - r)$ and Q will have moved half this length, $\pi(R - r)$. At the same time P will have moved a distance of $2\pi R$ so that the transmission factor of Q relative to P is

$$\frac{\pi(R - r)}{2\pi R} = \frac{R - r}{2R}$$

which can be made very small by making $(R - r)$ small. For example when $R = 10$cm and $r = 9\frac{1}{2}$cm then

$$\frac{R - r}{2R} = \frac{1}{40}$$

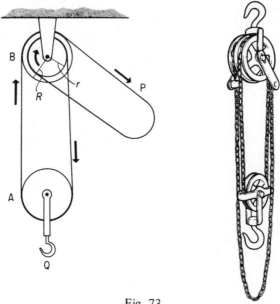

Fig. 73

This type of pulley, as illustrated, is usually used with a chain which tends to make it very inefficient but it is commonly used in engineering workshops for lifting heavy loads.

Hydraulic Systems

As machinery becomes more complex it often becomes more sophisticated and new technology may enable simpler solutions to design problems. One major revolution has been the proliferation of mechanisms involving hydraulic rams, some of which we saw in the chapter on linkages where they were used on heavy civil engineering equipment.

The system in Fig. 74 consists of a piston P moving in a cylinder A connected to a cylinder B in which is a second piston Q. The pistons are tightly sealed and between them is a fluid whose volume can be assumed to remain constant.

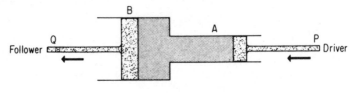

Fig. 74

Suppose the cross sectional areas of cylinders A and B are 20cm^2, and 60cm^2 respectively. Then when P moves forward 1cm it pushes 20cm^3 (volume of cylinder = area of base x height) of fluid into cylinder B so that piston Q must move $\frac{1}{3}$ cm to increase the effective volume of B by 20cm^3.

The linear transmission factor of Q relative to P, in this case, is thus $\frac{1}{3}$ and as the system is very efficient it means that any force applied to P becomes multiplied by 3 for the output at Q.

The great advantage of the hydraulic system is that the cylinders A and B do not have to be adjacent or parallel but can be connected by a length of small bore flexible pressure tubing. Fig. 75 shows a system with a transmission factor of $\frac{1}{80}$. Note that the pressure of the fluid is the same everywhere and is equal to 5kgf per square centimetre.

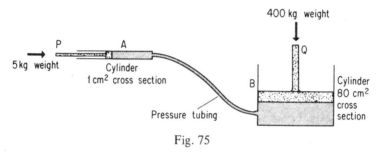

Fig. 75

Design a hydraulic system capable of supplying an output force of 2400 kgf from an input of 30 kgf if the pressure tubing can safely withstand any pressure up to 20 kgf per square centimetre.

Another great advantage of the hydraulic system is the way in which several outputs can be operated from one input. This is seen in the braking system of a car where one piston operated by the brake pedal supplies fluid to pistons inside each brake drum (see Fig. 76 and Fig. 87).

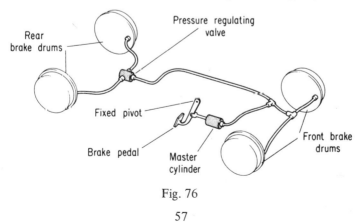

Fig. 76

57

The clutch of a modern car is also operated by a hydraulic ram as are most of the wing tabs and other movable surfaces of a jet airliner.

As with the pulley system a hydraulic ram can convert a small force moving a relatively long distance into a large force moving a small distance. Such large forces are made possible by this process that giant hydraulic presses can be made to shape steel ingots as we might press plasticine.

In recent years the BMC have introduced hydrolastic suspension to some of their cars. This is shown diagrammatically in Fig. 77.

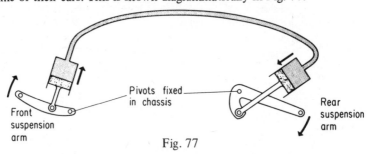

Fig. 77

As the front wheel hits a bump the fluid is pushed out of the front cylinder into the rear one thus allowing the front wheel to rise and keeping the rear wheel in contact with the road while the car remains on an even keel.

A hydraulic system of a sort is used in an air gun where air in a cylinder of relatively large diameter is expelled into a barrel of very small bore where the pellet acts as the piston until it is ejected.

This chapter has much in common with some traditional Physics and Mechanics but it must be emphasised that its inclusion here is because the main design consderations are geometrical.

With both pulley systems and hydraulic systems the ratio of the distances moved by the driver and the follower can be calculated from the geometry of the system.

In this work, the fact that this ratio is closely connected to the mechanical advantage of the system is of secondary consideration.

Rotary Motion to Linear Motion

Most mechanisms consist of a variety of moving parts in which linear and rotary motions are interconnected.

The part which is the source of the motion is called the driver and the part which comes at the end of the train of moving parts, whose motion we are particularly concerned with, is called the follower. Often the driver consists of a pulley or gear wheel on the shaft of a constant speed motor and it is the job of the engineer to design a mechanism to perform a specific movement in the follower.

This might be, for example, just another constant speed shaft as in a lathe, or a mechanism to provide an oscillating movement as in a sewing machine, or a mechanism to tie a knot in a piece of string as in a baler.

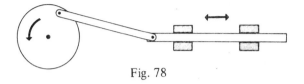

Fig. 78

In a car engine linear motion is converted into rotary motion by means of a crank shaft and connecting rod while the same mechanism is used in reverse to operate a pump, move the needle in a sewing machine or provide the vibration to the shaking tables at a mill for separating tin from its ore.

In a planing machine in a joiner's shop the mechanism, for moving the cutting blades, is shown in Fig. 79. A motor drives the flywheel at constant speed and a pin on this wheel engages in a slot in the rod OQ. When the pin is in the major sector AB (see Fig. 79(b)) the rod is driving the cutting tool through the wood but when it is in the minor sector AB it is returning the tool for a fresh cut.

This means that the time taken to return the cutting blade, the wasted time, is shorter than the time spent cutting. A saving in time like this over many years can mean a tremendous financial saving on just one machine compared to one driven by the mechanism such as that in Fig. 78 where the return time would be equal to the cutting time.

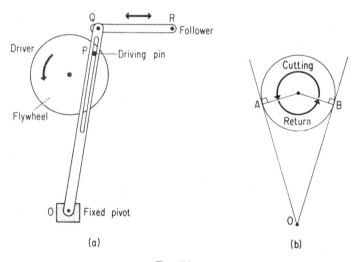

(a)   (b)

Fig. 79

59

Rotary motion is converted into linear motion whenever we turn the handle or key to unlock a door, while a screw is another familiar object which has this effect.

In all these cases we could analyse the number of turns needed to achieve a given linear movement and so compare them.

Vices, clamps and car jacks are further examples of the screw's use.

Another common device for converting rotary motion to linear motion is the rack and pinion (see Fig. 80). It is used in two distinct ways.

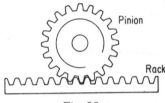

Fig. 80

In one the rack is fixed so that the pinion moves forward over the rack. In this form it is used in mountain railways to stop the engine slipping or to move a tool carrier on a lathe or move a drilling platform to the required height. Alternatively, the pinion rotates about a fixed shaft and the rack slides along its own length as, for example, in some window opening mechanism and door bolts, or the focusing mechanism of a microscope.

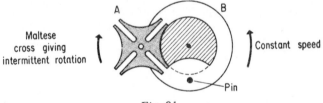

Fig. 81

Motion pictures are made possible by an ingenious device which enables the film to be pulled past the gate, one frame at a time. The mechanism, shown in Fig. 81, consists of a 'maltese cross', A, which is turned quickly when the pin on wheel B engages in one of its slots, and then held still until the pin comes around again. The film is moved by sprockets on the same shaft as A, designed so that every time A turns through $90°$ a new frame is pulled in front of the gate. When the film is moving a shutter covers the gate and cuts off the light to the screen. As soon as the film stops moving the shutter moves to let the light through. When we look at the screen we are not aware of these changes because the eye takes a longer time to stop seeing a picture than it takes to change from one frame to the next.

Try to make a model of this mechanism using hardboard or plywood — it is not too difficult if made on a large scale.

Investigate the various mechanisms in a camera for operating the shutter and winding on the film.

Levers

The lever comes in all forms in mechanisms big and small.

Fig. 82 shows sketches of brake levers but essentially any jointed rod with a fixed pivot is a lever.

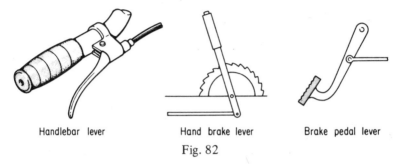

Handlebar lever   Hand brake lever   Brake pedal lever

Fig. 82

Often levers are attached to wires as shown in Fig. 83 and then the linear transmission factor of Q relative to P depends on the lengths OB and OA where O is the fixed pivot.

Give approximate transmission factors for Q relative to P for each case illustrated.

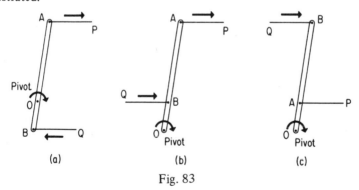

(a)   (b)   (c)

Fig. 83

The railway signalling systems were a fine example of the use of levers and wires to transmit motion and they often employed 'bent' levers known as bell cranks to change the direction of the motion (see Fig. 84). One familiar example for boys is the mechanism used to operate the tail flap of model control line planes.

61

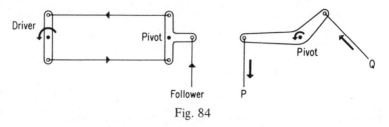

Fig. 84

The capstan winch is a good example of the use of a lever to convert rotary motion into linear motion. The larger the pole (see Fig. 85) the smaller the transmission factor and hence the bigger the force which can be given to the rope by the person pushing at P.

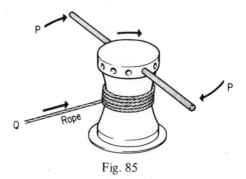

Fig. 85

Levers working in tandem are to be found commonly, for example as scissors, pliers, nutcrackers and in caliper cycle brakes.

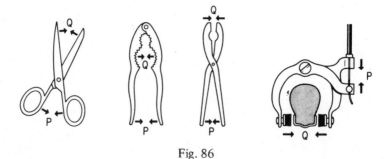

Fig. 86

Why is it easier to cut with a pair of scissors when the material is near to the pivot?

The caliper brakes are a way of turning a 'scissor' action through a right angle. Garden shears with long handles for trimming edges of lawns have a similar design.

62

Examine the way in which levers are used in the mechanisms of different pianos both in the way the keys are connected to the hammers and the way the pedal operates. How does a typewriter work?

Many instruments both scientific and domestic make use of levers. From kitchen and bathroom scales to the more sophisticated scales to be found in a chemist shop, or a large weighbridge for lorries, all rely on systems of levers. Delicate instruments such as the aneroid barometer also use levers to magnify small movements so that they are easily observable.

In what way is a wheel barrow a lever?

Miscellaneous Mechanisms

We saw earlier how the brake drums of a car are connected to the foot brake by a hydraulic system, but we did not see how the brake in fact worked.

It is interesting in passing, to note that the hand brake only operates on the rear wheels and does so by means of a wire transmission. Three methods of moving the brake shoes into contact with the brake drum are shown in Fig. 87.

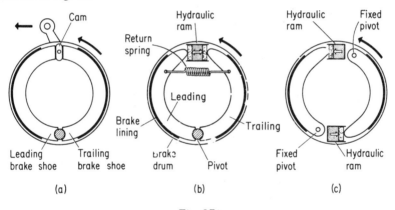

Fig. 87

The way in which the shoes move towards the brake drum in (a) and (b) are similar, only the driver is different. In these designs one shoe (labelled leading) bites into the drum as it turns while the other (labelled trailing) is pushed away by the drum so is not so effective. This is overcome by (c) where both shoes are arranged to be leading. This last would not be nearly so effective in reverse however — mind the kerb when doing a 3 point turn! In all these cases the brake shoes are pulled away from the brake drum by springs when the brake is released.

One motion which puzzled the authors for some time was that of the 'bucket' of the cranes often seen around town for mending street lights

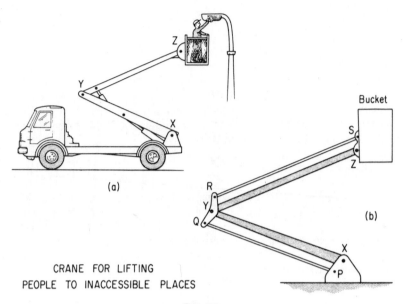

(a)

(b)

CRANE FOR LIFTING
PEOPLE TO INACCESSIBLE PLACES

Fig. 88

(see Fig. 88(a)). The way in which hydraulic rams opened out the 'elbow' XYZ was easy to understand but not the way in which the bucket stayed upright regardless of the angle of YZ to the horizontal — that it does so is of course vital for the man inside. The secret is to make use of two parallelogram linkages joined by a bell crank (see Fig. 88(b)). Because QYXP is a parallelogram, QY is always parallel to PX, which is itself fixed in direction. The crank QYR is thus always at the same angle and because RSZY is a parallelogram this in turn implies that SZ is always parallel to RY.

It is instructive to make a model of this linkage to observe just what happens as XYZ is opened out — the result is in many ways more satisfying than the above geometrical argument.

This chapter has hardly begun to look at the mechanisms involved in machinery but it is hoped that we have done enough to interest you and open your eyes to the possibilities. A visit to a printing works, or a flour mill or a machine shop should pose enough questions to keep you occupied for a long time while a visit to a car factory or textile mill could supply enough mathematics for the whole school course. For the historically minded there is a large field to explore in industrial design under the heading of 'Industrial Archaeology' where some of the early sources of power and machines provide a fascinating study and the problems to be solved were clearly seen.

Fairgrounds, building sites, civil engineering undertakings, docks, garages, farms, factories, the dentist's surgery ... are endless sources of situations where machines and mechanisms are to be found and the thesis of this book is that their design is largely based on geometrical principles which is not so much a case of being able to quote a geometrical theorem but of being able to appreciate shapes in motion and their relation to one another.

THE PUPILS' MATHEMATICS

Underlying much of this chapter is an appreciation of the lever and this can be studied in terms of the relative *movement* of its parts rather than by the relative forces which can be balanced. A significant property of all mechanisms is the way in which the *follower* moves in response to a movement in the *driver*. Often the driver is a constant speed motor, and it is the designer's problem to use it to generate an entirely different motion. In the simpler mechanisms (e.g. pulley systems) there is a direct ratio between the distances moved by the driver and follower, which can be thought of as a scale factor and compared to the gear ratio of the last chapter. When this is the case the work can lead to arithmetic calculations, but much of the work in this chapter will lead to descriptions of mechanisms and, for most pupils, the spatial work will be more qualitative than quantitative.

The work on levers can be done with the materials used for the linkages but the work on pulley systems needs specialised apparatus which might be borrowed from the science department.

Any work on hydraulic mechanisms is likely to be rather theoretical and should only be done if motivated by a study of machinery where it is seen to be significant. When this is the case it leads to useful work on area and volume. Some experiments are possible though if two pumps, say a cycle pump and a car pump, are joined by a tube filled with water — where there is a will there is a way!

We envisage a visit to a machine shop, printing works, textile mill or other environment rich in mechanisms as a way of stimulating interest in this work.

The cards which follow indicate the main types of activity which stem from this chapter. Cards on pulley systems have been left out because we found it difficult to write them without knowing the specific equipment available, but this should present little difficulty.

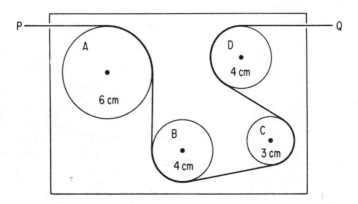

Set up 4 pulleys on a base and pass a string around them as shown.

Keep the string taut and move P 10cm to the left.

1. How far does Q move?
2. Which pulleys turn clockwise?
3. Which pulley turns twice as fast as A?
4. Do any pulleys turn at the same speed?

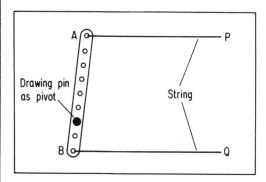

Pin a 9-hole strip to a board as shown and tie a piece of string to each end.

1. When Q is moved 4cm to the right how does P move?
2. When P is moved 9cm to the right how does Q move?
   Repeat for different distances.
   Plot your results graphically.
   What can you say about the movement of P and Q?
   Put the drawing pin in another hole and repeat the above experiment.

If is is thought that this card attempts too much it could be made into two or more. It may be helpful to make a table (and or plot a graph) for a lot of different movements with the pivot at the same position. This is illustrated with the next card which considers a lever pivoted at one end.

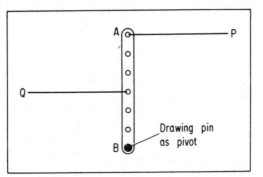

Pin a 7-hole strip to a board and tie pieces of string as shown.

Move P 1cm to the right and measure the distance moved by Q. Enter the result in a table like the one below.

Repeat for movements of 2cm, 3cm, 4cm, 5cm, 6cm, 7cm, and 8cm.

Distance moved to right	
by P	by Q
1 cm	
2 cm	
3 cm	

Plot your results on a graph.
What do you observe?

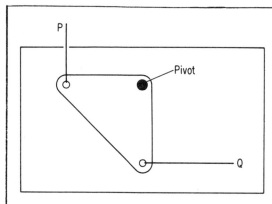

Pin a bell crank to
a board and attach
strings as shown.

1. When Q moves to the right in which direction does P move?
2. Move Q 5cm to the right.
   How far does P move?
3. Where have you seen this mechanism used?

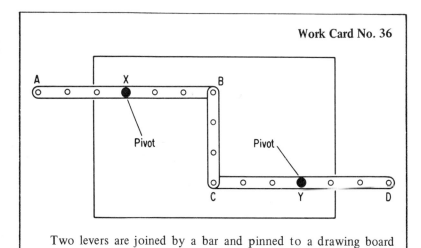

Two levers are joined by a bar and pinned to a drawing board
as shown.
Describe the movement of D as A moves down.
How is this movement altered if Y is moved nearer to C?

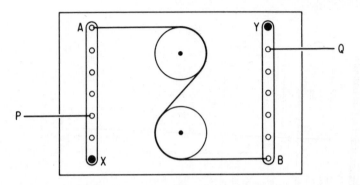

Two 7-hole levers are fixed to turn about one end on a board as shown. Their free ends are connected by a string which passes around two pulleys.

Move P 6cm to the left.

1. How far does A move?
2. How far does B move?
3. How far does Q move?

   What is the transmission factor?

Work Card No. 38

Design a mechanism to connect two strings so that when one is pulled the other moves 3 times as far and at right-angles to the first.

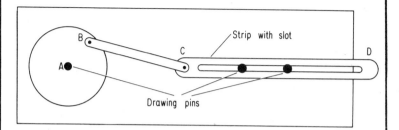

Mount on a drawing board the linkage shown. Place the drawing pins carefully so that the wheel can make complete revolutions without the strip CD jamming.

1. Turn the wheel around and describe the movement of CD.
2. How does the movement of CD vary if you change
   (a) the size of the wheel,
   (b) the length of the rod BC?
3. Where do you find this mechanism?

Work Card No. 40

Examine the braking system of a bicycle (or car) and explain carefully, with drawings, how the movement of the brake lever is transmitted to the movement of the brake shoes.

Work Card No. 41

Describe how linear motion is converted into rotary motion in two of the following:
   (a) A lawn mower,
   (b) a roller blind,
   (c) an American screwdriver or push drill,
   (d) a carpet sweeper,
   (e) a steam engine.

Examine one of the following and describe how it works. Make drawings of the important mechanisms.
  (a) a cycle bell,
  (b) a tin opener,
  (c) a water tap,
  (d) a retractable ball point pen,
  (e) a lock.

Investigate how mechanisms have influenced one of the following:
  (a) argicultural work,
  (b) domestic work,
  (c) civil engineering,
  (d) physically handicapped people,
  (e) transport.

5

Shapes for a Purpose

The object of this chapter is to analyse shapes which have been designed to fulfil a specific purpose and see how this will enable us to design shapes ourselves to perform specific functions.

The drawings in Fig. 89 show a vertical rod which is free to slide up and down in a fixed sleeve. The rod in each case rests on a shape which rotates about a fixed axis.

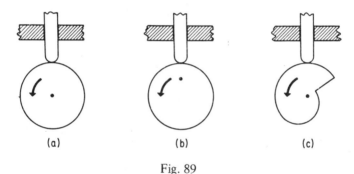

Fig. 89

Describe the motion of the rod in each case as the shaft carrying the shape rotates at a uniform speed. Sketch graphs to show how the height of the rod above the sleeve changes with the angle turned through by the shape.

What would happen if the shapes were rotated in a clockwise direction?

Shapes like this are known as *cams* and have a large variety of applications in mechanisms. From the examples above it should be clear that by varying the shape of the cam an infinite number of variations can be produced in the vertical motion of the rod. In a car engine for example a whole series of such cams are all mounted on the same shaft (the cam shaft) and actuate the inlet and exhaust valves of each cylinder.

Fig. 90 shows a cam as used by a sewing machine for threading cotton on to a spool. This arrangement enables the cotton to be wound on to the reel in a uniform manner. For every revolution of the spool the worm gear turns the spur gear carrying the cam teeth on. The cam, in turn, pushes against the cotton guide moving it to and fro at an even speed.

73

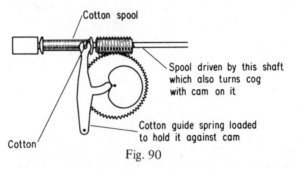

Cotton spool

Spool driven by this shaft which also turns cog with cam on it

Cotton guide spring loaded to hold it against cam

Cotton

Fig. 90

Rotary switches are also designed to be operated by cams. As the cam in Fig. 91 rotates, it closes the switch contacts and completes the circuit so that the bulb lights. When the cam turns further round the contacts spring apart. Design a cam which when turning at a uniform speed will make the bulb have a sequence of: long flash, short flash, short flash repeated.

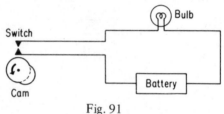

Bulb

Switch

Cam

Battery

Fig. 91

Suppose a lighthouse had a light pattern of: on for 10 seconds, off for 10 seconds, on for 5 seconds, off for 5 seconds. How could a rotary switch be designed to give this effect?

Describe what happens to light A and light B (see Fig. 92) as the cam turns through one revolution.

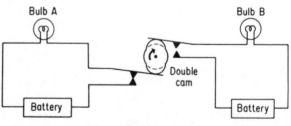

Bulb A

Bulb B

Double cam

Battery

Battery

Fig. 92

Analyse the light sequence and timing of some local traffic lights and design three cams to operate on switches for the red, amber and green.

There is a lot of scope here for practical work and the design of cams to give a desired light sequence gives an insight into the properties of rotating shapes.

The contact breaker in the distributor of a car engine gives a good example of a switch operated by a cam (see Fig. 93).

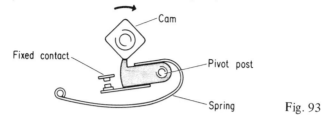

Fig. 93

A very similar method is used in the mechanism for a barrel organ or a musical box. A rotating drum has tiny pins projecting from it which come into contact and 'pluck' metal reeds as they turn (see Fig. 94). Each note has a reed corresponding to it and as the drum rotates the chords played will correspond to the pins which have been fixed to the drum.

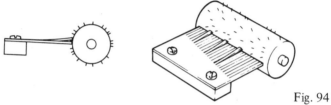

Fig. 94

How does a chiming clock produce its tune?

Ratchets

A mechanism which allows free rotation in one direction but not the reverse direction has many applications as for example in the free wheel of a bicycle, in a winch, the winding mechanism of a clock, or in a lawn mower. The basic principle of the ratchet is illustrated in Fig. 95. The small 'cam' on the outside of the wheel is sprung in towards the wheel and does not effect the anticlockwise motion but will stop clockwise motion. Through what angle might the wheel be allowed to turn before being stopped? How could the mechanism be designed to decrease this angle?

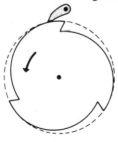

Fig. 95

The mechanism in a lawn mower which allows the blades to go on revolving after the large driving wheels are stopped is simple but ingenious (see Fig. 96).

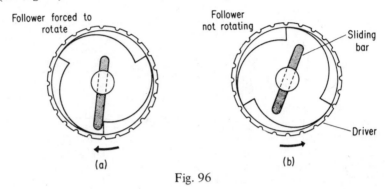

Fig. 96

As the driver turns clockwise one of its three protruding lugs will engage with the sliding bar of the follower (Fig. 96(a)). No spring is necessary, the shape of the lugs of the driver is sufficient. If the driver stops or turns the other way the bar slides to and fro in the follower but does not engage with the driver (Fig. 96(b)).

Mechanisms for fastening a door have the same ideas incorporated.

The drawings in Fig. 97 show some of the devices which allow a door to shut but prevent it opening — there are many others.

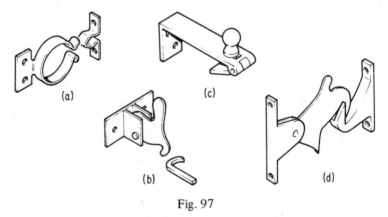

Fig. 97

The design of keys and locks is a study in itself and is full of mechanisms involving cams and ratchets. The subject has not been expanded here but would certainly be a useful topic for a project which could be approached from many points of view including the historical one.

76

One excellent source of examples the authors have found for much of this work is to obtain from a builder's merchant a slightly out of date catalogue which is issued to him by his supplier. These catalogues illustrate in great detail anything a builder's merchant is ever likely to need and with measurements and prices given provide realistic source material for say an investigation into door fastenings or a project to fit central heating into a house.

Curves of Constant Breadth

When the rollers pictured in Fig. 98 roll forward one metre how far forward does the slab AB move if there is no slipping at the rolling surface?

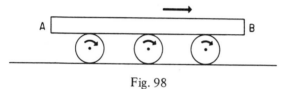

Fig. 98

When rollers are used to move heavy objects we always use rollers with circular section and it might be supposed that that is the only possible shape. However when we analyse the situation it can be seen that the property required of the shape is that it should always have the same height no matter how it is turned. Surprisingly there is an infinity of possibilities of curves with this property: they are known as the curves of constant breadth.

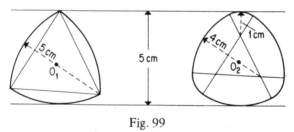

Fig. 99

Two such shapes are illustrated (not full size) in Fig. 99. For pupil use, they should be based on equilateral triangles of sides 5cm or larger O_1 and O_2 the 'centres' of each triangle should be located and marked. When cut out of card or hardboard the pupils can investigate what happens when:

(a) the shapes are turned around between two parallel lines 5cm apart;
(b) the shapes are turned around inside a 5 centimetre square hole (see Fig. 100).

77

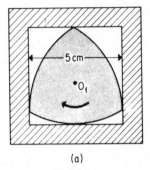 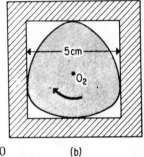

(a)   Fig. 100   (b)

By putting a pencil point through the shapes, the paths of O_1 and O_2 can be traced as the shapes are used as rollers or turned inside a square.

Why could not the shapes be used as wheels?

The 50p coin is an example of a seven sided curve of constant breadth.

Such shapes have been used as the basis of a drill for cutting square holes (see Fig. 101).

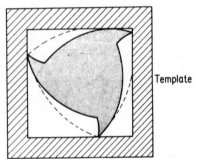

Template

Fig. 101

The drill turns inside a square template and is driven by a flexible shaft (like a dentist's drill). If you make a copy of the drill and turn it you will see that all but the very corners of the square are removed.

Curves of constant breadth need not even have symmetry. The shapes in Fig. 102 no matter how they are turned can always be made to touch a pair of parallel lines 5 centimetres apart. Try and see!

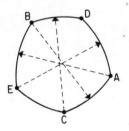 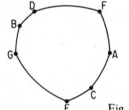

Fig. 102

To construct these shapes take a compass and with centre A and radius 5 centimetres draw an arc BE. Keep the radius fixed and draw further arcs with centres at B, C, D, E . . . until the shape is closed.

Both the shapes in Fig. 102 are formed of an odd number of arcs. Is it possible to make one with 4 or 6 arcs?

Do they all touch each side of a square at the same time?

The first shape in Fig. 99 has recently become very important as the cross-section of the rotor of the latest design in engines, the N.S.U.–Wankel rotary engine which has the tremendous advantage of no reciprocating pistons (see Fig. 103). A similar design was used as early as 1901 for a steam engine but the difficulty, then as now, is to maintain a satisfactory seal between the rotor and the cylinder walls.

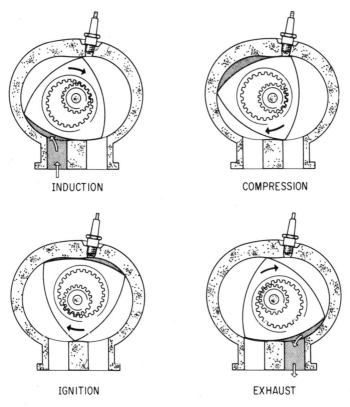

INDUCTION   COMPRESSION

IGNITION   EXHAUST

Fig. 103

Rotary Pumps

The rotation of a rotor inside a cylinder where the volumes of the regions change is the basis of most rotary pumps.

The vacuum pump in Fog. 104 has a rotor which turns about a fixed axis and two vanes which are kept against the outer walls by a spring between them. What is the greatest variation in the length of the vanes as typified by AB?

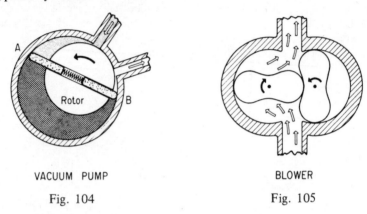

VACUUM PUMP	BLOWER
Fig. 104	Fig. 105

The blower in Fig. 105 relies on accurate machining of its two rotors which are geared to turn together so that they are always touching. The shapes of these rotors are examples of conjugate curves. (The design of such curves is interesting but would require too long an explanation at this stage.)

The Parabola

Because of its intrinsic geometrical properties the parabola occurs as the solution to many physical problems. The designer of telescopes (radio or light) or car headlights or electric fires sees it as the ideal shape for reflecting a parallel beam of energy.

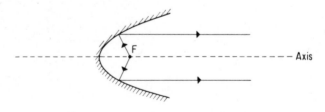

Fig. 106

If a source of light is put at the focus, F, of the reflector, Fig. 106, then it is reflected from the surface in a direction parallel to the axis. Conversely if a parallel beam of light (such as that from a distant star) is collected by the reflector it is all focused to F enabling a very faint object to be observed.

The main cables on a suspension bridge take up the shape of a parabola when completed although because of the varying loads during construction this is not always the case. The bridge engineers however have to calculate on the basis of a parabola where to attach the cables which hang down to the carriageway. If the vertical cables are attached at equal distances along the carriageway they will not be attached at equal intervals along the main cable. There is scope for experiment here using small weights tied to strings.

Civil engineers take great care to design our roads to suit the high speed of modern traffic and in designing a curve to join one straight to another they do not use a circle as you might have guessed, but a parabola. There are several reasons for this but the most important one is that it is safer, as it eases a car into and out of a bend, while it is easy to lay out by offsets.

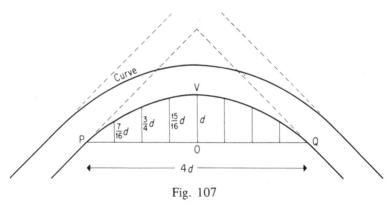

Fig. 107

In Fig. 107 the construction is shown for a 'right angles' bend. A line is set up across the bend and an offset OV pegged from its mid point a quarter of the length of PQ. Further offsets are pegged at equal intervals between P and Q of length $\frac{7}{16}$ of OV, $\frac{3}{4}$ of OV and $\frac{15}{16}$ of OV. The outer bend is obtained as a translation of the inner bend.

Apart from these uses the parabola occurs (approximately — the curve is in fact affected by air resistance) as the path of a jet of water from a hose or of a shell from a gun — when you look along the sights of a rifle the barrel is invariably pointing above the object being aimed at. When a cricket ball is returned from the outfield to the wicket-keeper there are

81

many possible trajectories, but all are approximate parabolas, the difference depending on the speed and angle of the throw.

Cones

Cones, or at least truncated cones, occur for many purposes: as funnels, for ice cream, as corks or glass bottle stoppers, as valves in an engine, as lamp shades, as part of the bearing for a cycle wheel, as beakers to name but a few and it is interesting to see what geometrical property is significant in these uses.

Valve   Lamp shade   Glass stopper

Fig. 108

If several glass stoppers are available to fit a glass bottle, what would you need to look for to ensure a good fit?

Suppose you had a wire frame for a lamp shade in the shape of a truncated cone (a cone with its top cut off, the cut being parallel to the base) and wished to cut out some material to cover it. Is it possible to do this without getting creases in the material? What shape would you cut out? (Hint — put the lampshade on its side and roll it!)

A significant feature of a truncated cone as used for ice cream tubs for example is that when empty they readily fit inside one another and save space; contrast this with the space wasted in storing empty jam jars.

Miscellaneous Shapes

This last section is little more than a haphazard jotting down of other fields to explore which have many possibilities.

(a) The shapes of tools. Why is a spanner the shape it is? What advantage have hexagonal headed nuts over square headed nuts? Why is a plough designed in the was it is? Examine a sewing machine and try to understand how it works.

(b) Space filling — the best shape to make packages to economise on materials and space.

(c) Design of boats and planes — design of wings to obtain lift, design of boat hulls, sails and self-steering gear. Model planes.

(d) Furniture design. Working height for a table. Length of chair seat and angle of inclination. Design of unit furniture which can be fitted together to build up larger pieces. Stability and rigidity. Design of built-in furniture — for example given the dimensions of a bedroom, design a unit for one wall consisting of wardrobes and dressing table.

(e) Design the ground floor plan of a bungalow or design a petrol filling station.

(f) Water wheels, propellers, fans, turbines (rotors).

THE PUPILS' MATHEMATICS

Most of the work on cams is concerned with what angle a cam has to turn through in order to become operative. The lighthouse question (p. 74) requires an understanding that the cam has to account for $10 + 10 + 5 + 5$ seconds of being either off or on, in other words each second counts for an angle of $360° \div 30$ (= $12°$) and so a suitable cam which turned once every 30 seconds would look like this (Fig. 109):

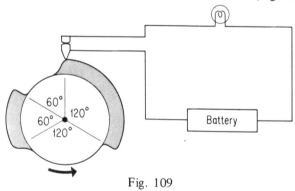

Fig. 109

Ratchets for the same reason involve angles. The ratchet in Fig. 95 could turn clockwise through no more than $12°$ before being stopped.

The curves of constant breadth are of interest especially now that we have the 50p coin as an example of a seven sided version of such a curve. The fact that such curves always remain in contact with parallel lines drawn the appropriate distance apart comes as quite a surprise. The same effect is doubly so when rotated inside a square.

As was stated much of the work in this chapter is best dealt with under the heading of projects.

Space filling — not only the shape of the packages, but also their nets should be investigated. The latter when made from flat cardboard will have to include tabs for gluing. It is also worth considering containers for holding other containers. For instance, cylindrical tins could be packed in

83

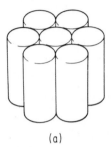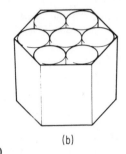

(a)   (b)

Fig. 110

groups of 7 and housed in a box with a hexagonal cross-section (Fig. 110). Several such boxes could of course be packed together with no waste of space. Pupils may well investigate such packings. For instance, investigate the boxes necessary for packing 9 tins together, or 12 tins together. Which would be the cheapest box to make (because it used least material per tin) – the '7 box', '9 box' or '12 box'? Are all these boxes space filling?

Packing spheres together is interesting, and one way of doing this is used in the design of egg trays.

Furniture design – there is scope here for a variety of ideas. The heights of tables and chairs has been mentioned but also of interest is the shape of table tops, seats and so forth. Unit furniture brings in the problem of fitting pieces together as does a study of stackable furniture.

Cutlery design – here the pupils should examine weight, length, point of balance and in the case of spoons, their capacity.

84

The following are a few examples of work cards.

Work Card No. 44

You will need: some cardboard wheels, paper, pencil, drawing pins.

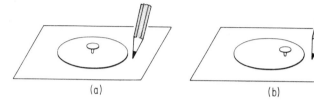

(a)   (b)

(a) Push a drawing pin through the centre of one of the wheels and pin it loosely to the paper. Make sure the wheel is free enough to rotate. Place a point of a pencil near the wheel. When the wheel is rotated does it push up against the pencil?

(b) Now loosely pin the wheel to the paper but with the pin going through the wheel at a point *not* the centre. Place your pencil point near the wheel as it revolves. Does the pencil have to be moved? If so, how far?

Work Card No. 45

You will need: a hardboard cam of the type shown and a pencil.

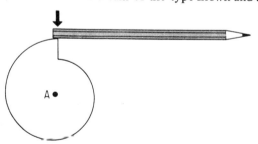

A •

Rotate the cam about its centre. Hold a pencil against the cam as shown pushing the end inwards towards A.

In what direction must the cam rotate?

What happens to the pencil as the cam rotates?

Work Card No. 46

You will need: a template of an equilateral triangle, paper, pencil, cardboard, scissors, ruler.

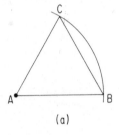

(a)

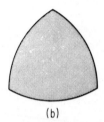

(b)

Draw around the triangle on the cardboard. Centre your compasses on A and draw an arc from C to B. Repeat for the other corners to obtain the shape in figure (b). Cut out this curved shape.

Work Card No. 47

You will need: the curved shape made in card 46, paper, pencil, ruler.

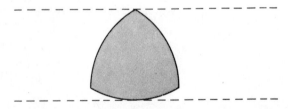

Lay the shape on your paper and draw two parallel lines as shown. Rotate the shape about between the parallel lines. Can you find a position it can go in and not touch the parallel lines? If you can, draw a new set of parallel lines that just touch the shape and try again.

You will need: hardboard rollers in the shape of the curve used in cards 46 and 47.

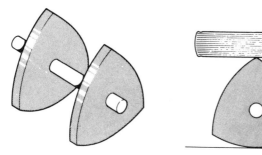

Roll the rollers along a flat surface. Why could you not use these instead of wheels? Lay a book on top of the rollers and push the book sideways allowing the roller to rotate. Does the roller make the book move up and down? In what way does the roller behave as a circle?

6

Loci

In any machinery there is bound to be a number of moving parts; whether they be cogs, wheels or merely rods. It is to these which we now turn our attention and study the wealth of curves and patterns which points on these moving parts trace out.

Imagine you were rolling a packing case over and over on its sides. In one revolution of the case the positions it would take up are shown in Fig. 111.

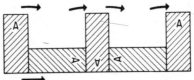

Fig. 111

What path would a point of the packing case trace out as you rolled it over? The dotted line in Fig. 112 shows the path of one point.

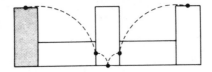

Fig. 112

Note the number of arcs in this curve is equal to the number of edges the case has turned about. What other points might it be interesting to examine? The choice might be a corner point or some internal point. Fig. 113 shows the trace of a corner point and it will be seen that now the number of arcs is one less than the number of edges that the case has turned about. The reason for this is that at one stage in the rolling the case is rotating about the point concerned and hence misses an arc.

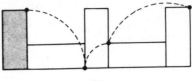

Fig. 113

What happens if the point chosen is somewhere on the end face but not on its edge? Fig. 114 shows the locus of just such a point.

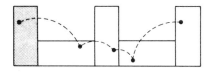

Fig. 114

Finally, the drawings in Fig. 115 show a series of loci for a number of different points. Note that if the point chosen lies on the vertical axis of symmetry, then the curve is symmetric.

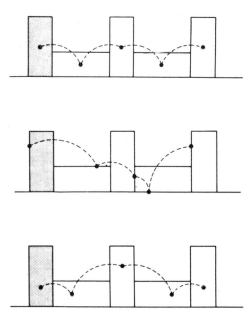

Fig. 115

Of course the packing case could have been of a different cross section and Fig. 116 illustrates a number of loci for points placed in different positions on the end face of a case whose cross section is that of an isosceles triangle.

89

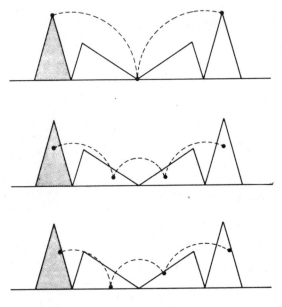

Fig. 116

All these curves are made up of a series of arcs of circles and may be produced either by rolling a shape along a straight edge and marking positions of a particular point for a number of closely spaced positions of the shape itself, as it rolls along the edge, or by considering the points about which it is rolling and using these to draw arcs from one position to another (see Fig. 117).

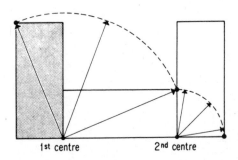

1st centre   2nd centre

Fig. 117

If we now replace the packing case with a wheel, a new group of interesting curves can be obtained. What are the three essentially different point positions to be studied here? They are an edge point, an internal point and an external point. The first is when the point lies on the circumference of the wheel. When the resulting locus is drawn it will be as in Fig. 118.

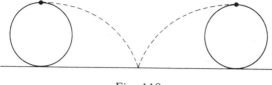

Fig. 118

With the point within the wheel itself then the curve will become that shown in Fig. 119.

Fig. 119

On the other hand when the point is carried on an arm attached to the wheel, a curve with a loop will be obtained as in Fig. 120.

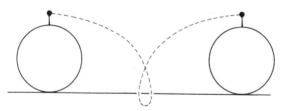

Fig. 120

This last case is the trace of a point on the flange of a railway wheel (see Fig. 121).

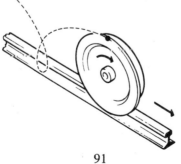

Fig. 121

These curves have several interesting properties, but before dealing with these, it might be as well to explain how in practice these curves may be produced. All that is needed is a thick strip of wood with a straight edge, a wheel with if possible a groove cut in its edge and a length of string. The string is wrapped round the wheel and its two ends pinned to the edge of the wood holding the string taut. The whole is laid flat on a piece of paper and the appropriate locus plotted for different positions of the wheel (see Fig. 122). It will be found that with a little care, slipping will be reduced to a minimum.

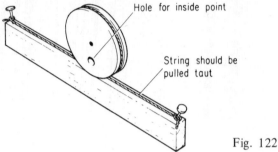

Hole for inside point

String should be pulled taut

Fig. 122

Fig. 123 (a) and (b) show different positions of the trace when the upper end point of a diameter is taken, and when the initial point of contact is considered.

Points for pupil investigation might well include:

(a) To compare the two traces.

(b) From Fig. 123(b) to find both the height and the span of the arch produced. The latter question may awaken memories of finding the circumference of a circle by rolling it along a line.

(c) There is a simple whole number relationship between the area under the arch and the area of the generating circle. Using squared paper to find the areas, this relationship may be determined.

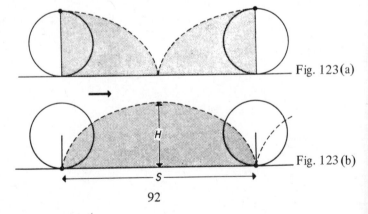

Fig. 123(a)

Fig. 123(b)

The study of a point on the circumference of the rolling circle may be followed by considering in like manner a point INSIDE the circle. Examples of this could include the motion of a spot (red label) on the wall of a car tyre, or the motion of the end of the valve on a bicycle wheel.

As a matter of interest, this same curve when used to form the face of a ramp as shown in Fig. 124 will allow a ball to roll down it in a shorter space of time than if the ramp had a straight face as seen in Fig. 125. Fig. 126 also shows a pair of ramps made like this but with the curved path allowed to run slightly up hill, here again the ball will get along this one faster.

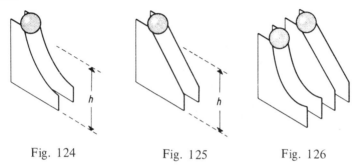

Fig. 124   Fig. 125   Fig. 126

The curves generated by studying the motion of a point on the circumference of a circle which rolls without slipping along a straight line are called CYCLOIDS. It must be appreciated that cycloids are not arcs of circles (or for that matter arcs of any of the other conic sections – ellipse, hyperbola, parabola). The pupil is thus meeting a new kind of curve with its own mathematical properties.

The length of the cycloid is also interesting. Find by experiment what this is. The results might suggest that it is in fact exactly four times the diameter of the generating circle.

So far we have rotated a circle along a straight line. Spirals can be drawn if the process is reversed, namely if the straight line is rolled over a circle (see Fig. 127).

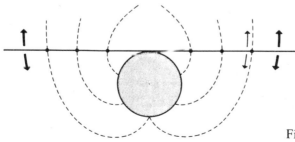

Fig. 127

It can be seen that one group of points form an unwinding spiral, the others a closing spiral. This is the simple see-saw.

An interesting toy on the market is the 'Spirograph'. Here, curves are produced by rolling one circle upon or inside another. If, as in Fig. 128 the outer circle is the same size as the inner, then three essentially different patterns can be produced for the three cases of internal, edge and external points.

It will be shown later that these curves can be drawn by other methods. Ideally the curves of Fig. 128 (called EPICYCLOIDS) are best drawn using cogs of the same size, but failing this two circular wheels with grooves on their edges may be used. A loop of string should be wrapped tightly round them in a figure eight to prevent as much slipping as possible (see Fig. 129).

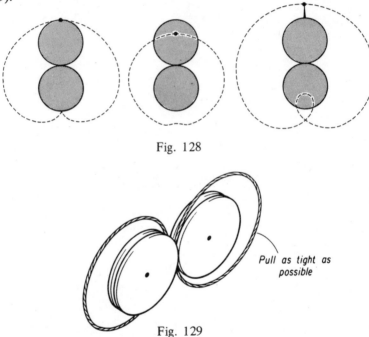

Fig. 128

Fig. 129

Pull as tight as possible

The next locus is only introduced on the assumption that an annular (or ring) cog is available for use. (Spirograph cogs are useful here). Here we have a circle rotating inside another, the internal circle being half the size of the external one (see Fig. 130). A point on the circumference of the internal circle will trace out a straight line. Some years ago engineers used this to produce straight line motion.

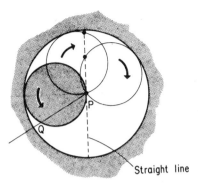

Fig. 130

What happens to the chord PQ as the inner circle rotates?

Many curves may be drawn using circles (cogs) of different sizes. If cogs are not available then these curves may be drawn using cardboard and a full description of this method is given in the chapter on 'The Work and its Presentation'.

The curves produced when one circle rolls inside another are called HYPOCYCLOIDS.

Cycloids, epicycloids and hypocycloids are easily and *quickly* drawn by using the Spirograph kit. The virtues and pleasures of free use of the apparatus should provide a starting point for the pupil. The wealth and variety of the fascinating patterns which may be produced must be crystallized if a mathematical study is to be enlightening. This will best be done by selecting the circles which provide simple whole number ratios of their diameters, and from thence progressing to the more difficult ratios and more involved patterns.

The following mathematical notes are probably sufficient to provide clues for teachers.

(a) A circle of radius b rolling without sliding on the *outside* of a circle of radius $n\,b$ produces an epicycloid. (When n is an integer we have an n-cusped epicycloid, i.e. an epicycloid with n 'petals').

Some special cases of epicycloids:

$n = 1$ produces a curve called a cardioid (heart shaped)

$n = 2$ produces a curve called a nephroid (kidney shaped)

(b) A circle of radius b rolling without sliding on the *inside* of a circle of radius $n\,b$ $(n > 1)$ produces a hypocycloid.

Some special cases of hypocycloids:

$n = 2$ produces a straight line

$n = 3$ produces a deltoid

$n = 4$ produces an astroid

95

The surprise is, of course, finding a straight line as a special case of a hypocycloid – an interesting case of continuity in mathematical pattern. Fig. 131 illustrates some examples of the curves that can be produced.

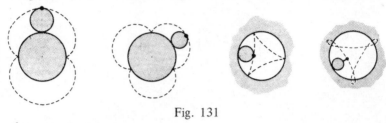

Fig. 131

How many times does the moving circle have to rotate around the fixed circle before the trace comes back on itself?

Up to now we have studied curves formed by things that do not slip. Now we will study curves traced by sliding or slipping rods. Suppose a rod fixed at an angle to a straight line be allowed to slide up and down it. The trace of points on the two arms of the sliding rod will be a series of parallel lines. What change would it make to this result if the angle to the fixed line was altered? (see Fig. 132).

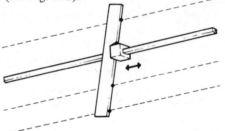

Fig. 132

Imagine a set up as shown in Fig. 133, here a rod as before can slide up and down a straight line but it is also made to pass through a fixed point R.

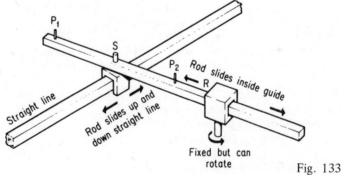

Fig. 133

We are interested in the loci of two points P_1 and P_2 fixed at equal distances from the point S. The resulting loci are shown in Fig. 134.

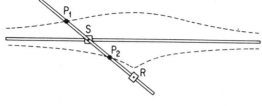

Fig. 134

This curve is called the conchoid of a straight line. If we now exchange the straight line for a circle and the point S is made to slide round the circle then under certain conditions we can draw the family of curves already mentioned, namely the epicycloids. (Here in fact we shall be drawing the conchoids of a circle). Fig. 135 illustrates three cases possible.

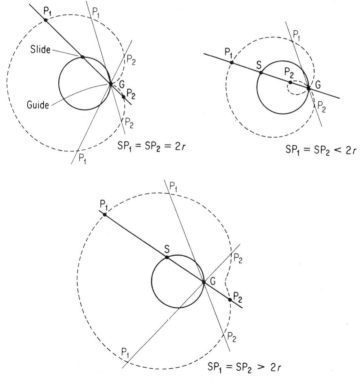

Fig. 135

In practice it is difficult to make apparatus that will draw all three curves but nevertheless they can be drawn very simply by using a ruler and placing it, so that it always passes through G and then measuring off from the circumference of the circle the required fixed distances from P_1 and P_2. If close positions for the ruler are taken the resulting locus will be apparent.

Rolling, sliding and slipping, these are our three main headings so far and this last group of ideas concerned both sliding and slipping but what about slipping alone? All of us at some stage in our lives must have climbed a long ladder and half way up wondered what would happen if the top of the ladder came away from the wall. The answer is easy, we would trace out a neat curve (circle) centred at the foot of the ladder until we hit the ground with the ladder on top of us! The other possibility, and the one more likely is that the bottom of the ladder will slip outwards. Fig. 136 shows four different positions of such a ladder. If we concern ourselves with every point on the ladder then the resulting locus will be an area formed by the sum of all the curves put together (see Fig. 137). Notice that here we have used the word locus for the set of points swept out by a line segment with the result that we obtain a two dimensional locus.

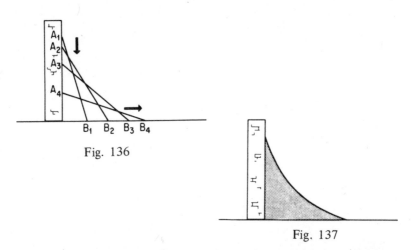

Fig. 136

Fig. 137

The trace of individual points on the slipping ladder needs investigating. What special cases will be interesting? There are three, a point on the end, a non centre point and finally the centre point. An end point will trace out a straight line, down the wall or along the ground. A non centre point is shown in Fig. 138. Fig. 139 illustrates that of a centre point. What is this curve? To produce these curves all that is needed is a right angle drawn on paper and fit a straight edge in the position of a ladder.

98

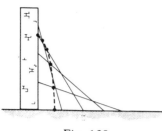

Fig. 138

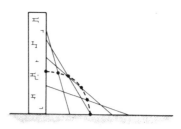

Fig. 139

Fig. 140 illustrates a more practical approach.

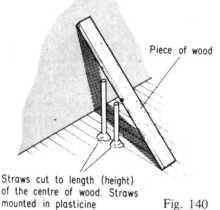

Straws cut to length (height)
of the centre of wood. Straws
mounted in plasticine

Fig. 140

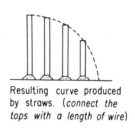

Resulting curve produced
by straws. (*connect the*
tops with a length of wire)

Whilst on the subject of ladders it is worth examining some of the facts associated with that type of step ladder as illustrated in Fig. 141. The obvious question arises, namely what happens if the rope is cut? Assuming each section slips uniformly then what path does the top trace out? What about a point half way up the steps? The answers to these questions are essentially the same as if it was a simple ladder leaning against a wall. The diagrams in Fig. 142 show the results. In practice however the two sections do not slip uniformly and thus rather than study difficult situations of both slipping unevenly let us put one end against a wall as shown in Fig. 143.

Fig. 141

99

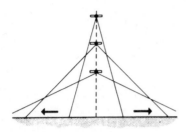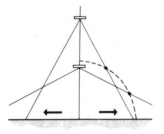

Fig. 142

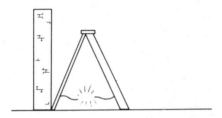

Fig. 143

We could examine all the interesting cases by looking at an isosceles triangle as it is opened out but here surely is a case for using the real thing. Place a step ladder alongside a wall and fix one set of feet. Untie the securing rope and open out the feet stage by stage whilst at the same time noting where on the wall your chosen point lies (see Fig. 144).

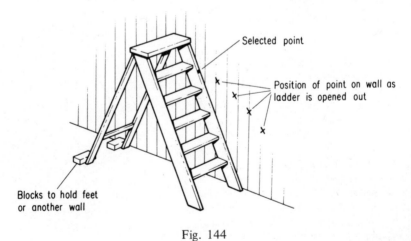

Selected point

Position of point on wall as ladder is opened out

Blocks to hold feet or another wall

Fig. 144

100

In considering the step ladder we have in fact touched on the ideas behind two types of car jack. Both are illustrated in Fig. 145.

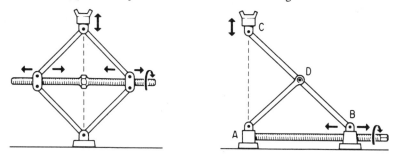

Fig. 145

Whilst these jacks have been considered in the chapter on linkages it is nevertheless worth noting here that this subject could be studied from either point of view. The second type, namely that which uses a triangle with an extended side has critical measurements. Make a simple linkage as shown in Fig. 146 and study the loci of several points on the arm CD. Why is it necessary in the case of the car jack for CD to equal DB? (AD = DB)

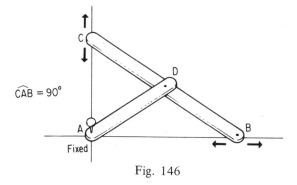

$\widehat{CAB} = 90°$

Fig. 146

Two important ideas in plane geometry can be illustrated by the next two examples of slipping. We take the example of a triangle being allowed to slip about between two fixed pegs as shown in Fig. 147.

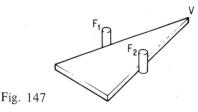

Fig. 147

Fig. 148

The answer to the question of what will be the locus of the vertex of the triangle is of course a circle that passes through the pegs (see Fig. 148). What types of triangles should be studied? What theorem is demonstrated in each case? If the angle at the vertex is not a right angle then the theorem shown is that of angles in the same segment. If the vertex is right angled then the theorem is that of angles in a semi circle. The second after all only being a special case of the first.

Although much movement in real life situations is three dimensional it can often be studied two dimensionally. (Compare plans and elevations for a house). To take a simple example, what is the trace of a pedal of a bicycle when it is cycled along a flat surface? Here we are interested in motion in a vertical plane. In relationship to the cycle itself the locus is of course a circle but in relationship to the ground it is a cycloidal curve. To find this by experiment a bicycle should be slowly moved over a flat surface and the position of the pedal at several small intervals noted. Rods (straws, dowels, etc.) cut to the appropriate length should be mounted at the appropriate positions. Fig. 149 illustrates the method.

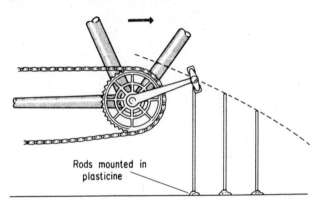

Rods mounted in plasticine

Fig. 149

If a cycle with gears is used then different traces for the pedal will be recorded for different gears. This experiment is well worth the effort.

An example of three dimensional tracing is that of the T crane so often to be seen in use on building sites (see Fig. 150). What is the path traced out by the hook of the crane when it is hoisting an object up whilst at the same time swinging around?

A model of just such a crane can quite easily be made and providing it can be made to lift and swing at the same time the rest of the work is simple. As before, straws can be used to show the trace of the hook as illustrated in Fig. 151.

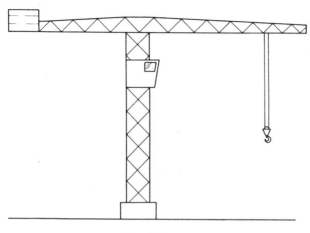

Fig. 150

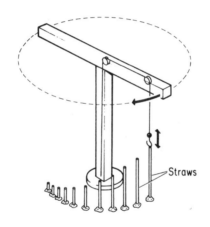

Straws

Fig. 151

The experimental approach, whereby a locus can be tracked or traced experimentally, not only provides an approach well suited to the less academically minded pupil but it also can serve as an introduction to loci for those pupils who will take the matter further by deductive methods.

THE PUPILS' MATHEMATICS

In this chapter we have looked at a few loci not normally considered in traditional geometry. Nevertheless all occur in everyday life.

What is the locus of a point which moves so that it is always the same distance from a fixed straight line? Most of us know that the answer is a pair of lines parallel to the first and at an appropriate distance away. We could however deduce the answer by looking at a few particular positions that the point could take up. The missing points could then be filled in by common sense. It is this approach that

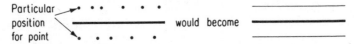

Particular position for point would become

we use in this chapter. The pupil discovers a few special positions for some moving point and from these deduces the remaining locus.

The rolling packing case introduces these ideas. It might well be felt important also to study how far a rectangle, triangle or circle move in one revolution. Often the relationship of the perimeter to the distance rolled is assumed to be obvious. To some pupils this is not the case.

The rolling wheel idea with an entirely new curve in the shape of the cycloid offers not only the interest of the curved shapes themselves but also an opportunity to revise ideas on methods of finding curve lengths and non-rectangular areas.

The essential difference between a circle and any other curve of constant breadth lies in the fact that with a circle the radius is constant whilst in the case of a non-circular roller this is not so. The locus of their respective centres when they are rolled along a flat surface shows this (Fig. 152).

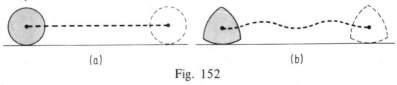

(a)   (b)

Fig. 152

The conchoids of a line and circle have been shown since their construction needs the minimum of apparatus. Here again a full locus is built up from taking a number of positions the points could take up and filling in the missing ones. When $SP_1 = SP_2 = 2r$ or the constant distance equal to the diameter, we get the special case, the curve known as a cardioid.

The slipping ladder has been included since the locus of the centre as the ladder slips is surprisingly a quarter circle centred on the foot of the wall. Another example of a special case being of interest.

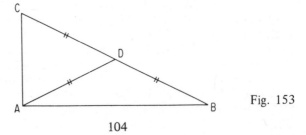

Fig. 153

Given the figure as shown with CD = DA = DB, the question has often been asked, prove the angle CAB is a right-angle. One solution uses the fact that C, A and B will always lie on a circle centre D. Since CDB is a straight line it forms the diameter of this circle and CÂB is thus an angle in a semi circle and is therefore a right-angle. The car jack uses this idea, namely that if AB is parallel to the ground, no matter how long AB is made, then C will always lie on the upright arm of the right-angle.

The angle in a semi circle is also studied by using a right-angled triangle to slip between two fixed pegs.

Materials used for this chapter need neither be complicated nor expensive.

Packing case rolling — hardboard or wooden shapes are best since holes are easily drilled and the shape itself is more durable than cardboard.

The cycloids — in the long run it is but to make a series of wheels cut to specific easy diameters (such as 2cm, 4cm, 5cm, etc.). This enables comparisons between diameter and length of curve or diameter and area to be made more easily. Spirograph wheels used in conjunction with the straight track supplied are ideal for eliminating slipping but they are rather small.

Epicycloids, hypocycloids — if Spirograph wheels are not available then cardboard discs have to be used. It is best if the stationary disc is glued down.

The following work cards are a guide as to how some of the ideas of this chapter may be presented to pupils.

You will need: a hardboard rectangle, ruler, paper, pencil.

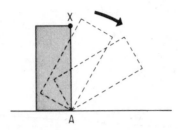

Hold your ruler flat on a piece of paper. Roll the hardboard rectangle about a corner as shown in the figure. Do not let the corner A slip. Trace round the rectangle in a number of different positions as it rolls.

What path does X move along until the rectangle is flat on its side? Now, try it with matchboxes of various sizes.

You will need: a hardboard rectangle, ruler, paper, pencil.

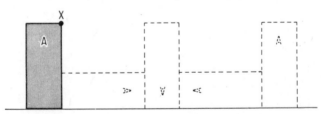

Place your rectangle against your ruler flat on the page. Mark where X is on the paper. Roll the rectangle a small amount. Mark where X is now. Roll the rectangle a bit more. Mark the position of X. Continue this until the rectangle has rolled upright again. What path has X moved along? How many corners have you used as turning points?

You will need: a rectangle with a small hole drilled in it, a ruler, paper, pencil.

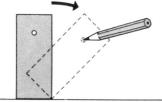

Place your pencil point in the hole in the rectangle. Roll the rectangle over and over along the edge of the ruler. Your pencil traces out the path taken by the hole as the rectangle rolls. What happens if you start with the rectangle the other way up?

You will need: a hardboard triangle, ruler, paper, pencil.

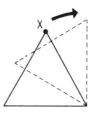

Roll the triangle along the edge of your ruler.
Find the path X traces out as the triangle rolls over and over.

You will need: a circular disc, ruler, paper, pencil.

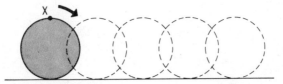

Place the disc against the edge of your ruler. Mark a point X on the disc and where it lies on the paper. Roll the wheel a very small amount along the ruler. Mark on the paper where X is now. Roll the wheel again a small amount. Mark where X is. Go on doing this until the wheel has rolled a complete revolution.

Mark in colour the path X has traced out in this rolling.

You will need: a circular disc with a hole drilled near its edge, ruler, paper, pencil.

Place your pencil in the hole and roll the wheel to find the path traced out by the hole as the wheel rolls along the ruler's edge.

Compare the result with your answer for work card No. 53.

What difference do you notice?

You will need: a circular disc with a hole drilled in its centre, a ruler, paper and a pencil.

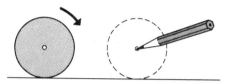

What will the path traced out by the hole look like when the disc rolls along your ruler's edge?

Check your answer by placing your pencil in the hole and tracing out the path as the wheel rolls. Compare this result with those for cards 53 and 54.

You will need: a triangular non-circular roller with a hole drilled in its centre, ruler, paper and a pencil.

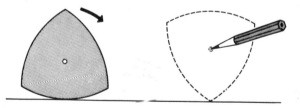

Draw the path traced out by the centre hole by placing a pencil in it and rolling the roller along the edge of your ruler. What is the difference between this result and that for card No. 55?

Why is a circular wheel better than one of this shape?

You will need: circular discs of diameters, 4cm, 6cm, 8cm, string, ruler, paper and a pencil.

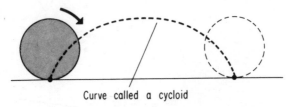

Curve called a cycloid

Roll one of the discs along your ruler and find the path traced out by a point on its circumference when the disc rolls exactly once. Measure using the string the length of this path. Repeat for the other discs.

Fill in this table:

Diameter of disc	Length of curve
4cm	
6cm	
8cm	

Can you find any connection between the diameter of the disc and the length of the curve called a cycloid.

110

You will need: circular discs, ruler, squared paper and a pencil.

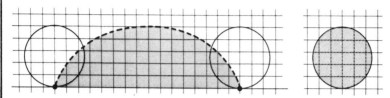

Roll one of the discs along your ruler and find the path traced out by a point on its circumference when the disc rolls exactly once.

Count the number of squares enclosed by the cycloid (the shaded area).

Draw around a disc and count the squares it covers, to find its area.

Fill in this table for as many discs as you want:

Area of cycloid	Area of disc

Can you find a connection between the area of the cycloid and that of its disc?

You will need: 2 cogs of the same size, paper and pencils.

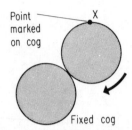

Place one cog in the centre of your paper. Mark a point on the other cog. Rotate one cog around the fixed one and find the path X takes. Draw the actual path.

You will need: 2 equal cogs, one with a hole drilled in it, paper and pencil.

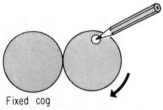

Rotate the cog with the hole round the other cog and by placing a pencil point in the hole find the path it traces out as the cog moves right round the fixed cog.

What is the difference in shape between the locus of the hole and that of the last card?

You will need: a ruler, paper and pencil.

Draw a line 10cm long in the centre of your paper.
Mark a point which is 4cm away from the line.
What other points are 4cm away from the line?
Say in words where points have to be in order that they are always 4cm from the line.

You will need: a long straight strip of wood, a ruler, paper and pencil.

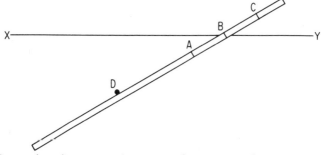

Mark on the strip of wood near one end the three points as shown.

Draw a long line across the centre of your paper. Letter its ends X and Y. Mark a point D on the paper about 6cm from the line. Lay your wooden strip on the paper as shown with B on the line and the edge of the strip passing through D. Mark on the paper where A and C are. Repeat for different positions of the strip. What is the locus of A and C? Remember that the strip *always* touches D, and that B is always on the line XY.

You will need: a set square, a ruler, paper, pencil.

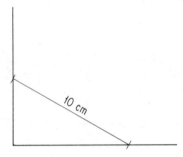

Draw a right-angle and extend the arms of the angle. Fit a line 10cm long in between the arms of the angle as shown. Draw the line. Find as many positions as you can for this line making sure that the ends always touch the arms of the angle. Draw it in each time.

You will need: a set square, ruler, paper and pencil, strip of wood 10cm long.

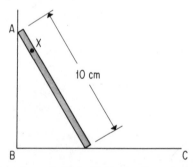

Draw a right-angle and fit in between the arms of the angle the piece of wood. Mark a point a short distance from the top end as shown. Mark where the point lies on the paper. Move the wood to another position keeping its ends on the lines. Again mark where the point X lies on the paper. Repeat this again and again until the strip is lying flat along BC. Draw in the complete path that X traces out as the strip slips between the arms of the angle.

You will need: a set square, ruler, pencil, strip of wood with a hole cut in its mid point.

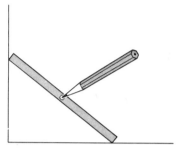

Draw a right-angle. Fit the strip in between the arms of the angle. Place the tip of the pencil in the hole and slip the wood about so that it always lies in contact with the arms of the angle.

What path does the centre trace out as the wood moves from being upright to lying flat?

Work Card No. 66

You will need: a hardboard triangle, paper, pencil.

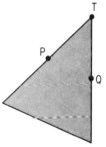

Place the triangle on the paper and mark two points P and Q as shown. Find where the vertex T of the triangle can move if the sides of the triangle always touch the points P and Q.

What difference is made if the angle at T is 90°?

Book List and Other References

This list is inevitably limited as the book attempts to do something original. The best source of ideas comes from just being observant and jotting down ideas on a piece of paper or as you find them. Any additions to the material in the book and good references will be welcomed.

Cundy and Rollett, *Mathematical Models* (Oxford)

Leonard Holmes (Editor), *Odhams New Motor Manual* (Odhams)

Life Science Library, *Machines*

Dean Lent, *Analysis and Design of Mechanisms* (Prentice Hall)

W. W. Sawyer (Editor), *Mathematics in Theory and Practice* (Odhams)

Steinhaus, *Mathematical Snapshots* (Oxford)

Northrop, *Riddles in Mathematics* (Pelican)

A Catalogue from M.A.C. (The Metal Agencies Co. Ltd., Bristol).

Magazines are helpful as are brochures from industrial firms on their products.

The Motor, The Autocar, The Meccano Magazine, and the *Aeromodeller* are a few magazines which will contain useful ideas, but any magazine related to engineering, building, agriculture, industry and domestic equipment should be found helpful.

Television programmes such as 'Tomorrow's World' and 'Tom Tom' also contain stimulating ideas.

Museums, particularly the British Science Museum are an unending source of ideas showing how man through the ages has designed mechanisms and shapes to fulfil a great variety of purposes.